Cognitive Psychology

Methods Companion

Cognitive Psychology
Methods Companion

Edited by Helen Kaye

Contents in brief

Contents

Introduction

What is cognitive psychology? While it would be impossible to answer this question without describing its subject matter – the various topics that cognitive psychologists study – equally indispensable would be a description of the various methods that it adopts. The characteristics which distinguish cognitive psychology from, say, philosophy of mind or linguistics include the range of empirically based methods that cognitive psychologists use. Over the past quarter-century there has been a sea change in that range of methods, with an ever-increasing reliance on methods that have a neural basis. This book focuses on two of these non-experimental methods of cognitive psychology, as well as including topics that relate closely to the use of experiments, such as ethics and the use of quantitative methods.

Ethics

In Chapter 1, Bundy Mackintosh discusses the importance of adopting and adhering to ethical principles in conducting research. Although many cognitive psychological studies raise few major ethical concerns, it would be a mistake to think that none do, or that some studies raise no ethical considerations. In conducting studies with human participants, all researchers need to be aware of the ethical dimension that links them and their participants. The chapter begins with a philosophical distinction between deontological and consequentialist approaches to ethics, separating the intrinsic morality of the method and that of its consequences. Mackintosh then outlines some of the key ethical issues of which psychologists must be aware when conducting research. The chapter also discusses the ethical codes of the British Psychological Society (BPS) and the American Psychological Association (APA), which are accessible from the DD303 website.

Neuroimaging

In Chapter 2, Ingrid Johnsrude and Olaf Hauk introduce neuroimaging, which is a rapidly developing field, with many techniques having being developed and many in development. The authors describe a number of different techniques for imaging the brain's activity, representing visually the changes in the brain that accompany cognition. Each technique depends on being able first to detect the activity of neurons by some means, and second to generate a measure of the activity. The measure can then be used to provide images displaying the spatial or temporal locus of neuronal activity and to support statistical analysis.

The authors concentrate primarily on EEG, MEG, PET and fMRI, outlining the limitations and advantages of these techniques.

Much controversy still surrounds the use of neuroimaging evidence. As becomes apparent in the course of the chapter, the different means for measuring neuronal activity are limited. For example, EEG and MEG have good temporal but poor spatial resolution – they are better at determining when neuronal activity takes place than exactly where. The reverse pattern holds for PET and fMRI. Such limitations – and many more are discussed in the chapter – remind us that neuroimaging techniques are informative only to the extent that we are prepared to draw inferences from the data they provide to the nature of cognitive processes, and that the validity of these inferences depends on many assumptions being satisfied. One thing that all the techniques have in common is that they measure physical qualities of neuronal activity. However, cognitive processes are usually cast in terms of information processing, which begs the question: how can we be sure that physical activity is the vestigial trace of cognitive activity; that the physical signs we observe correspond to cognition?

Of course, researchers have developed strategies to make sure their inferences are reliable. By comparing the images deriving from the performance of tasks that differ in just one component, for example, researchers can be more confident that the physical activity they see reflects the cognitive activity required by that task component. However, you can perhaps sense the difficulties involved by trying a simple thought experiment. Imagine trying to produce physical images of a computer's activity. You could perhaps produce images of your laptop's electrical or magnetic activity during a word-processing task; you might find that particular regions were active in certain tasks and not others. But it is hard to see how the images alone would tell you exactly what information processing the computer was performing. How would we know it was word processing and not calculating values and formulae in a spreadsheet? To draw those kinds of inference we would need some prior knowledge of the information-processing characteristics of the task and how those information-processing properties relate to the hardware involved. That is, at the very least, we would need a good information-processing model. In psychology, neuroimaging data are similarly likely to prove useful only to the extent that we already possess good cognitive models. This is not to say neuroimaging data are not useful – they can help us discriminate between models that make different predictions concerning the locus and type of cognitive processes involved in certain tasks, and they may continue to throw up new data implying the involvement of unanticipated processes in tasks that were thought to be well understood. Nevertheless, just how important neuroimaging data will prove for understanding cognition remains to be seen.

Cognitive neuropsychology

In Chapter 3, Ashok Jansari introduces cognitive neuropsychology, which is a field with a long history, having developed from a mix of research and clinically related concerns. The chapter introduces the topic in the context of its historical development, indicating the evolution and multiplicity of the goals of neuropsychology, and the varied techniques that neuropsychologists use to understand a patient's impairment and its possible significance for models of cognition.

To sense some of the complexity involved, this time you might like to imagine trying to work out the information-processing characteristics of your computer from an analysis of its errors. More often than not, it is extremely difficult to gain an understanding of information processing from observing just one (impaired) computer. Perhaps through observing many different computers, and systematically observing the patterns of impairment, one might ultimately begin to uncover some of the structure of their information processes. Whatever the inherent difficulties the strategy faces, this is the position of the cognitive neuropsychologist with regard to human information processing or cognition.

The difficulty of drawing inferences from patterns of impairment to the nature of cognitive processes is much reduced by making certain assumptions, and the author discusses a number of these – subtractivity, for example. The chapter also details many of the techniques used by neuropsychologists, such as standardized tests and the use of experiments. The chapter deliberately avoids in-depth discussion of some techniques that are being increasingly used by neuropsychologists, however. Neuroimaging is frequently used in conjunction with neuropsychological findings, often providing researchers with converging evidence from different sources.

Quantitative methods

In Chapter 4, Martin Le Voi offers what can be described as a conceptual treatment of statistical techniques for analysing data. All of the foregoing chapters in this book assume that, at some point in the research process, data will be gathered and analysed, and the appropriateness of an interpretation will depend in large part on the results of that analysis. Throughout the main textbook too you will encounter psychological findings that are based on the quantitative analysis of data. Sound statistical analysis provides a firm foundation for our knowledge of cognitive psychology; however, for many people, statistical analysis seems off-putting. For some, it is chock-full of intimidating formulae and algebra; for others, the conceptual underpinnings of the techniques are obscure. Chapter 4 introduces the key concepts needed by psychologists in an accessible way that only minimally relies on mathematical competence or confidence. From these beginnings, a number of different types of analysis are introduced, as well as some of their accompanying assumptions and limitations.

Chapter 4 includes reference to two kinds of computer-based exercise: spreadsheet exercises and SPSS exercises. Both types have been designed to assist students' understanding of the material covered in the chapter.

Spreadsheet exercises
Two formats of spreadsheet are available: Microsoft Excel and Oracle Open Office. DD303 students who do not have Excel can download Open Office from the Computing Guide accessible from their StudentHome page.

SPSS exercises
To run these exercises you will need access to a computer running SPSS/PASW. This software can be found on the SPSS/PASW DVD-ROM, together with the SPSS data files for the exercises. Note: it is assumed that the reader already possesses some familiarity with using SPSS, and the exercises in Chapter 4 do not give detailed guidance on how to conduct analyses in SPSS. If further guidance is needed, readers should consult one of the many SPSS guides available. One such book is Coolican, H. (2009) *Research Methods and Statistics in Psychology* (London, Hodder Education). You will also find a guide to SPSS on the DD303 website.

Once installed, SPSS data files referred to in Chapter 4 can be found by default in the folder C:\DD303\SPSS data.

And experimentation?

You may be surprised to find that experimentation does not feature in this volume as a topic in its own right; it is, after all, the most common research tool in cognitive psychology. You will however learn a good deal about the method through the project work included in DD303 and by your participation in residential school. Arguably the best way to learn about experimentation is by the hands-on experience of doing experiments. Hence, the focus in this volume is on methods for which student practical work would be impracticable and/or unethical, such as neuropsychology and neuroimaging; and those aspects related to the experimental method that can be studied outside the laboratory, such as ethics and quantitative methods.

Using this book

This volume has been designed to accompany DD303 *Cognitive psychology* and serves as a companion volume to the main textbook, *Cognitive Psychology*, edited by Helen Kaye. The Module Guide on the DD303 website will guide you in how to integrate your study of this book with that of the main textbook.

Two further related readings are available only as electronic files on the DD303 website. They are Reading 1, 'Connectionism', by Martin Le Voi and Reading 2, 'Symbolic modelling' by Paul Mulholland and Stuart Watt. Guidance will be given on the DD303 website as to when they should be referred to.

Chapter structure

Each chapter of this *Methods Companion* has been structured according to certain conventions.

An emboldened term signifies the introduction of a key concept or term that is either explicitly or implicitly defined in the surrounding text. Each chapter contains a number of activities. Often these may be simple thought exercises that may take no more than a minute or so. Others are more involved. Each activity has been integrated into the design of the chapter, and is aimed at enhancing your understanding of the material. We recommend that student readers attempt as many of these activities as possible and, where appropriate, revisit them after completing each chapter.

The chapters in this book make use of text boxes. Each box has been written to amplify a particular aspect of the material without interrupting the ongoing narrative. Though the boxes illuminate a wide range of issues, some focus on aspects of research studies and methods. You may wish to finish a section before reading a particular box.

Each substantive main section finishes with a section summary, often a bullet point list reminding the student of the key points established in that section. We hope that these will act as useful barometers of your understanding and encourage you to re-read sections where you don't follow the summary points.

Each chapter makes a number of explicit links to other chapters in the book, often to specific numbered sections, and sometimes to chapters in the main textbook (i.e. *Cognitive Psychology*). It would be tedious in the extreme to continually follow each and every link, flicking to the relevant pages and reading the relevant 'linked' section. Rather, these links are intended to emphasize the interconnected nature of cognitive psychology, and identify connections between topics that otherwise might seem disparate. Of course, we hope that you will be motivated to follow some of these links either on first reading, or on a later reading, perhaps as a revision aid.

As well as a list of references, each chapter ends with some specific suggestions for further reading. While each chapter is designed to be self-contained, inevitably some issues get less attention than they deserve, and so interested readers may wish to pursue some of these suggestions for a more in-depth treatment. Moreover, it is always worth approaching a topic from more than one direction – consulting different texts, including other general texts on cognitive psychology, can help achieve a richer understanding and we recommend this approach to all students. Chapters 2 and 3 each direct you to a supplementary journal article which you should read as part of your DD303 study.

Cognitive Psychology Module Team

This book was designed and produced for The Open University module DD303 *Cognitive psychology*. The editor gratefully thanks all those people, listed below, who have been involved in the process (based at The Open University, unless otherwise stated).

ORIGINAL DD303 TEAM:
    Module Chair: Nick Braisby
    Curriculum Manager: Ingrid Slack
    Core Team Members: Sandy Aitkenhead; Nicola Brace; Angus Gellatly; Alison J. K. Green; Martin Le Voi; Bundy Mackintosh; Peter Naish; Graham Pike

Curriculum Manager (rights): Ann Tolley
Curriculum Assistants: Marie Morris; Elaine Richardson
Additional Authors: Jackie Andrade (University of Sheffield); Peter Ayton (City University); Chris Barry (University of Essex); Simon Bignell (University of Essex); Martin A. Conway (University of Durham); Graham Edgar (University of Gloucestershire); Simon Garrod (University of Glasgow); Gareth Gaskell (University of York); Ken Gilhooly (University of Paisley); Olaf Hauk (MRC Cognition and Brain Sciences Unit); Graham J. Hitch (University of York); Emily A. Holmes (MRC Cognition and Brain Sciences Unit); Ashok Jansari (University of East London); Helen Kaye; Paul Mulholland; Mike Oaksford (Cardiff University); Mike Pilling; John Richardson; Andrew Rutherford (Keele University); Anthony J. Sanford (University of Glasgow); Stella Tickle; Tony Stone (London South Bank University); Stuart Watt (Robert Gordon University); Jenny Yiend (MRC Cognition and Brain Sciences Unit)
Module Reader: Matt Lambon Ralph (University of Manchester)
External Assessor: James Hampton (City University)
Media Project Manager: Lynne Downey
Production and Presentation Administrator: Richard Golden
Copublishing Adviser: Jonathan Hunt
Lead Editor: Chris Wooldridge
Editors: Alison Edwards; Kathleen Calder; Winifred Power (Freelance)
Designers: Tammy Alexander; Alison Goslin; Diane Mole
Graphic Artists: Janis Gilbert; Sara Hack
Picture Researcher: Celia Hart
eMedia Quality Promoter: Roger Moore
Software Designers: Ian Every; Maurice Brown; David Morris
Rights Adviser: Alma Hales
Contracts Executives: Katie Meade; Sarah Gamman
Compositors: Pam Berry; Lisa Hale; Phillip Howe
Print Buyer Controller: Lene Connolly
Assistant Print Buyer: Dave Richings

DD303 TEAM FOR UPDATE:
 Module Chair: Helen Kaye
 Curriculum Managers: Lesley Adams; Andrew Marriott; Meridian
 Core Team Members: Alison J. K. Green; Peter Naish; Hayley Ness;
 Mark Smith
Curriculum Assistants: Kyra Proctor
Media Project Manager: Melanie Bayley
Production and Presentation Manager: Richard Golden
Copublishing Executive: David Vince
Media Developer (Editor): Richard Easterbrook
Media Developer (Graphic Designer): Paul Hillery
Media Developer (Graphic Artist): Howie Twiner
Media Developer (Interactive): Jason Jarratt
Indexer: Jackie Butterley (Freelance)
Proofreaders: Sue Betteridge and Chris Wooldridge (Freelance)
Rights Assistant: Margaret McManus
Media Assistants: Neil Paterson; Carly Smith
Service Administrator: Anh Huntington
Production Coordinator (AV): Marilyn Reed
Print Buyer: Lene Connolly
Assistant Print Buyer: Nikki Smith

Ethics

Chapter 1

Bundy Mackintosh

1   Introduction

Debate about the values and ethical concerns of research that makes use of animals or human participants, or may impact their mental or physical well-being, has a long history and a continually evolving influence on the research community. Perhaps confusingly, many texts in fields such as psychology, medicine or the biological sciences will contain references to studies that seem very disturbing to the reader by current standards and would almost certainly fail to pass the scrutiny of modern ethical screening. As a result, reading about the studies of other, possibly eminent, investigators cannot be guaranteed to provide a guide to designing suitable research in the present, let alone research which would meet the needs of any future requirements (see, for example, Box 1.1).

1.1

Famously unethical? Milgram's studies on obedience

In the 1960s and 1970s at Yale University in the USA, Milgram completed a series of experiments to explore obedience in ordinary volunteers recruited from the community by newspaper advertisements (Milgram, 1963, 1974). During the course of the study, volunteers were induced to deliver what they thought to be dangerously intense electric shocks to a fellow participant. If you are not familiar with these studies, then it might be worth reflecting at this point on what obedience rates you might predict. What proportion of ordinary men (Milgram's participants were all male) do you think would obey instructions in a university experiment that they believed would involve delivering an electric shock that was both painful and possibly injurious or even lethal to a fellow participant? Milgram asked just this question of staff and students at Yale. In case these individuals were not sufficiently expert at judging human behaviour, he also asked 40 psychiatrists the same question. The former thought 1 per cent and the latter thought only 0.1 per cent would continue the experiment to its conclusion. The surprising and controversial outcome was that 65 per cent of participants complied with *all* conditions of the experiment. Even after relocating the entire study to run-down premises in a nearby town and repeating the procedure without the authority imparted by a prestigious university and university professor, obedience rates remained at a staggering 50 per cent.

In brief, the design of Milgram's experiment was as follows:

Participants were recruited to take part in an experiment on 'learning', for which they were paid. On arrival they thought they were drawing lots with another participant to decide who would be 'learner' and who would be 'teacher' in the experiment (in reality the draw was rigged so that the participant who had answered the advertisement would become the 'teacher'; the other participant,

---

an actor working with the experimenter, became the 'learner'). The 'teacher' was to test the 'learner' on a paired-associate learning task. Errors were to be punished with an 'electric shock' through electrodes attached to the hands of the 'learner'. After each error the level of the electric shock was to be increased using switches on an elaborate 'hoax' electric generator console on which the higher levels of shock had labels such as 'danger', 'severe shock' and 'XXX' at the extreme end. The actor made many errors and cried out and protested as if they were receiving real electric shocks until the higher levels were reached, after which they fell silent. The experimenter instructed the participant to treat 'no response' to the paired-associate question as an error, which necessitated a further increase in shock level. That is, if the participant continued to the highest level of shock then the behaviour of the actor should have led the participant to believe that they might have electrocuted their fellow participant to the point of rendering them unconscious or even killing them. To be fair to the participants, many did question whether they should continue to the high levels of shock. At these points the experimenter instructed them to continue, with graded prompts to the effect that the experiment would be ruined if the participant did not continue. At the close of the session participants were fully debriefed. Despite the obvious distress that participants suffered in the course of this study, Milgram felt that the end justified the means. He felt his work provided profound insights into human nature and our understanding of the ability of ordinary humans to engage in, for instance, military atrocities, in the name of obedience.

ACTIVITY 1.1

Do you think Milgram's experiment (Box 1.1) would satisfy current ethical codes?

COMMENT

The answer is almost certainly 'no'. Participants were distressed by the experiment well beyond what they might have expected in their everyday lives. They were not able to give informed consent because they were misled about the procedures. They were not informed that they could withdraw at any point – on the contrary they were coerced into continuing.

Notions of informed consent and absence of harm lie at the centre of considerations about the ethical appropriateness of research. Those invited to participate in research should possess enough information to judge whether they wish to take part and, as a result of their participation, should not be left in a worse condition than when they began, either physically or emotionally. In the case of studies employing vulnerable participants, such as children, the elderly and those with learning disabilities, these safeguards should also extend to any carers. Such studies additionally raise issues concerning who should give informed consent to planned procedures.

Good ethical practice is not solely about making sure participants (and where relevant their carers) are treated with respect and protected from harm. The reputation of, and people's respect for, the researcher, their institution and the disciplines of psychology and the neurosciences in general are at stake. Adherence to ethical codes should not be seen as a hurdle to be jumped over. Ethical considerations force researchers to think about the *process* of conducting research, and not just research questions themselves. They therefore play a role in ensuring that research is professionally conducted and that participants not only enjoy the process but feel they are helping in some small way to further our knowledge and push back the frontiers of science. As with many enterprises, word of mouth has a powerful effect, so it is also in researchers' interests to pay attention to their participants' experience. Many areas of research could not proceed at all without the help of human participants. It would be foolish, therefore, to squander such a valuable resource; paying attention to ethical issues should ensure that both individual researchers and the profession as a whole do not do so.

The British Psychological Society (BPS) and the American Psychological Association (APA) publish ethical codes of conduct for psychologists which include sets of principles for conducting research with human participants (the BPS and APA guidelines are accessible from the DD303 website). Each organization expects its members to adhere to their guidelines, and the journals of each require all research accepted for publication to comply with these codes. Other countries, of course, have similar codes but at present the requirements of these two appear to dominate North American and European research in psychology and the neurosciences.

There has been a burgeoning of institutional structures to oversee ethical issues and most, perhaps all, universities and other institutions (such as hospitals and prisons) that carry out research with human participants or animals have their own ethical committees. These usually consist of a panel of experts, often also including laypersons, which may set rules that are more stringent and specific than those of the BPS or APA. Although it may be suggested by some that research ethics committees serve as much to protect institutions from litigation as to protect the interests of participants, their express purpose is to ensure that only worthwhile research that pays proper regard to the well-being of all concerned takes place. Funding bodies almost invariably insist on adherence to their own codes as well as requiring that local ethical clearance has been obtained before releasing funds, so that researchers must submit details of their project proposals (sometimes to several committees simultaneously) and obtain ethical approval before their work can go ahead. The complexity of this process is further confounded by the limited consensus about practice between different sets of guidelines and the sometimes quite idiosyncratic interpretation of them by ethics panel members. See Box 1.2 for discussion of some of the issues an ethics committee would expect to consider in deciding whether to approve a proposed research study.

1.2

Gaining approval from an ethics committee

Proposed studies have to be considered by at least one ethics committee; that is, a panel of experts (often including lay people) who are there to ensure that the study is worthwhile and that participants will not come to any harm as a result of participating in the research. Ethics committees are normally found in hospitals

→

(for research with patients), universities (for research involving both students and community volunteers), and prisons (for research with offenders). Research with children, the disabled or the elderly may fall under one of these or may involve additional bodies. Overlapping interests may mean permission has to be sought from more than one committee. For instance, if a university lecturer is conducting research with patients with brain injury, both the university and local NHS panels would be involved. Before a piece of research can proceed, researchers have to submit for approval a summary of their research proposal to their own and any other relevant ethics committee.

The proposal will usually indicate:

- details of the host institution

- the background and rationale of the study

- the proposed methodology

- the participant recruitment, payment and data collection procedure

- methods for obtaining informed consent

- the duration and number of sessions with each participant

- the materials that will be used

- any physical or psychological risks or distress the researcher expects the participant might encounter as a result of taking part in the study, and what measures will be taken to deal with them

- the proposed statistical analysis of the data

- who will have access to the data in original and/or anonymized form

- details of compliance with data protection legislation

- proposed dissemination of results

- specification of responsibilities for public indemnity

- the qualifications and experience of the investigator and/or research supervisor.

It is up to the researcher to submit to and obtain ethical clearance from an ethics panel. Once the proposal has been submitted the researcher may be invited to a meeting with the ethics committee where s/he would be asked to summarize the study and explain why it should be given ethical clearance. Ethics committee members can quiz the researcher on any aspect of the study and require that part (or all) of the study be amended before it can go ahead. If, however, the study appears to be straightforward and non-controversial, ethical clearance may be granted by post.

When getting to grips with the relevance of ethics to research and how to assess the ethical issues raised by particular studies, it is helpful to try to look at research proposals in the way that ethics committees do. This also helps to sharpen critical awareness of the whole research process.

Students are most certainly not immune from this scrutiny; indeed, it is a vital aspect of training to be a psychologist that students demonstrate sensitivity to ethical issues, and understanding of and compliance with all relevant guidelines.

It should be noted that this chapter does not attempt to consider the ethics of animal experiments in any detail. The ethics of using animals in research are both complex and controversial. The special conditions for research with, and the housing of, research animals in the UK and elsewhere is covered by stringent legal frameworks. Regulations are designed to minimize unnecessary discomfort to the animals commensurate with the benefits expected from the research. A full discussion of ethics in animal research probably also requires considering other forms of animal exploitation including methods of animal husbandry in food production, the treatment of working animals, the pet trade, and the effects on wild animals of disturbance, pollution and the destruction of natural habitats. These are very important issues. However, consideration of them would detract from the chapter's main aim of illuminating ethical questions as they relate to cognitive psychology – though cognitive psychology does make reference to work conducted with animals, research using human participants is the primary focus of study.

Summary of Section 1

- Ethical concerns have a long history and continue to influence the research community.
- Notions of informed consent and absence of harm lie at the centre of considerations about the ethical appropriateness of research.
- Adherence to ethical codes is important for the reputation of researchers and the discipline of psychology, and professional organizations such as the BPS and APA publish guidelines that their members are expected to follow.
- Before commencing a project, researchers must consider ethical aspects of their proposals and gain approval from one or more ethical committee.

2   Ethical approaches: deontology and consequentialism

A **deontological** approach to ethics focuses on the process of research itself and the intent and conduct of the investigator. This implies a set of principles that have a universal form driven by notions of honesty, justice, integrity and respect, that should be adhered to regardless of the place and circumstances surrounding any particular investigation. For example, consider the notion of 'informed consent'. Ethical considerations suggest that participants should freely give their agreement to the research process, understanding what processes will be involved. In addition, this might be assumed to encompass any consequences that could follow from publication or release of information into the public domain. In reality, some research questions require that participants cannot be fully informed of all details of the research procedures without, in the process, nullifying the potential outcomes.

Also, whilst an investigator certainly ought to take all possible steps to protect the identity and respect the sensitivity of their participants, it is not possible to anticipate all potential outcomes. It is also not reasonable to guarantee complete confidentiality if the participants themselves transgress laws or moral or ethical codes. Indeed there is a legal requirement on the part of researchers (and others) to pass on information concerning, for example, the abuse of children or other vulnerable individuals.

A **consequential** approach to ethics does not assume an inviolate set of rules, but regards the situation and the consequences of actions as of primary relevance. Concentrating on the outcomes of research, such as increased knowledge or later advantages, for instance relief of suffering, moves the researcher towards making a cost–benefit analysis. In the extreme, however, a position in which the ends justify the means could allow a dangerous precedent, opening the potential of justifying real harm to a few individuals in the knowledge that information thus obtained may bring substantial benefit to many. In effect, this is the legal standpoint that most Western cultures currently take towards research on animals, although it is clear that many individuals within these cultures strongly object to this position.

In reality, the tension between the deontological and consequential standpoints is usually resolved by taking a somewhat middle position, but the conflict between them can and does arise concerning some sensitive issues. The requirement therefore falls upon researchers, academics, and students to consider the full context of the ethical position within which research can take place and the often conflicting rights and responsibilities of a potentially wide range of affected parties extending well beyond the immediate confines of the research situation.

Summary of Section 2

- A deontological approach to ethics focuses on details of the research process itself, and whether underlying ethical principles have been adopted.
- A consequential approach to ethics considers the consequences or outcomes of research to be of primary relevance.
- Most ethics committees will combine both approaches when reaching their decisions.

3   Ethical issues

Ethical questions have become so central to thinking about research methodology that, even when only reading about the work of others, consideration of ethics will help make sense of particular design choices and maintain an awareness of the complex and ever-changing ethical climate within which psychologists necessarily work. Before embarking on research at any level, it is vital to consult and satisfy appropriate ethical guidelines and codes of conduct. In order to do so you will have to plough through the detailed and technical prose in which they are (necessarily) written. This chapter aims to highlight some of the important principles for research involving human participants whilst avoiding the minute detail and precise language that these guidelines need to employ.

Box 1.3 discusses a task, paired-associate learning, which is uncontroversial in itself but uses materials that raise ethical questions.

1.3

An uncontroversial task?

In a research procedure, the task itself may be uncontroversial but the choice of material may be sensitive. For example, examine the following sample instructions and materials for a paired-associate memory task that asks the participant to form mental images of the 'to be remembered' items. (Of course, instructions for the experiment proper would fully explain the purpose of the experiment and the requirement to later recall words.)

Sample instructions

In this study we are exploring the effects of different types of imagery on memory for pairs of words. We would like you to produce a vivid mental image of yourself associated with each of these word pairs and afterwards you will receive a list of the first words of the pairs and we will test your ability to recall the second word from each pair.

Sample materials

(a) 'Neutral' materials	(b) 'Emotional' materials
baby – bath	murder – rape
kettle – drink	death – grief
nail – hit	spider – face
pork – roast	torture – agony
sandwich – bite	slaughter – holocaust
pedestrian – crossing	
kitchen – sink	
bat – ball	
bleach – dustbin	
match – burn	

Comment

Other and more controversial materials could be used, such as swear words, sexually explicit words, racist insults and so on. Here we have chosen not even to provide examples in these categories – would it be ethical to do so?

For the task described, forming a mental image of oneself associated with the emotional items described might cause distress (as might imaging oneself associated with swear words, racist or sexually explicit words). Would some other task using this same material be more acceptable? Perhaps an emotional Stroop task might prove acceptable instead – in this task, participants try *not* to

⟶

read the words but are asked to name the colour of the ink in which the words are printed. (See, for example, **Yiend and Mackintosh, 2010**.)

However, any of the words listed above, and many in the categories where we have not listed words, are likely to appear with some regularity in the media. It should therefore be acceptable to make (careful) use of them provided participants have some warning of their nature. But as will already be clear there are no hard and fast rules about what is acceptable and what is not. In addition, different types of participant will vary in their sensitivity to materials; a spider phobic might be particularly vulnerable to the 'spider – face' example, for instance.

ACTIVITY 1.2

(a) Deciding whether material is ethically suitable is not at all straightforward, as Box 1.3 shows. Indeed, some of the words in the 'neutral' list might take on quite different meanings if the pairings were rearranged. Suppose a researcher wanted to conduct a similar experiment, but their 'neutral' materials consisted of the following paired associates:

bleach – drink

baby – burn

bat – bite

pedestrian – hit

Would asking participants to form mental images for such materials raise ethical concerns? Try to consider the arguments for and against, and judge whether you would wish to approve the study.

(b) Ethical objections were made by one ethical committee when the word 'pork' appeared in a list of words to be learned outside awareness on the grounds that it might offend some religious beliefs. Because presentation was to occur outside awareness the committee felt that the participants would be unable to object and therefore more than usual care was required. What would be your decision in this case?

3.1 Competence

Researchers are expected to work within the boundaries of their own competence. This applies not just in the context of administering certain research procedures, but also in terms of anticipating and dealing with their potential consequences. For example, when dealing with complex equipment, such as described in Chapter 2 on neuroimaging techniques, it is clearly vital that the researcher is able to attach electrodes safely and efficiently, or screen and prepare a participant for a brain scan. These procedures are often so specialized that, although the researcher must have a good notion of what is involved and the necessary safety issues, detailed aspects of the procedures might be devolved to other members of a research team, such as radiologists in the case of PET scans. The researcher's competence must therefore extend to knowing who else will be essential, or perhaps on call, before investigations can begin.

At the other end of the spectrum are procedures that require relatively trivial technical competence such as issuing questionnaires or observing behaviour. Since it is deceptively difficult to conduct good research using these methods, ethical considerations should also include whether there could be flaws that risk wasting the participants' time. It is often difficult, especially for those outside the research area, to judge whether the value of the research warrants the participant time spent. Ethics committees are therefore more likely to concentrate on how questionnaire length, content or wording, or the nature of the observations, might affect those involved. Appropriate competence in this sphere includes some anticipation of what might upset or offend – for instance, in the context of religious or local cultural values, or in terms of emotional reactions to materials.

Investigators need to be competent and professional in setting up and conducting their own research but it is equally important that they refrain from claiming or implying that they have qualifications, affiliations or skills that they do not possess. The general public are inclined to misunderstand the nature of a psychologist's specialist knowledge. Frequently, they mistakenly assume that psychologists are medically trained. Many are not entirely clear of the distinctions, if any, between psychiatry, psychotherapy, and psychology. As anyone calling themselves a psychologist or admitting to studying the topic is likely to have discovered, the uninitiated can often assume they have almost magical abilities. Psychologists may be expected to offer insights on problems ranging from 'how to train my dog', 'how to solve family relationship problems', or 'how to be happy' to 'how to stop my child misbehaving at school'. In addition, psychologists are not infrequently expected to possess a superhuman ability to mind-read and uncover people's innermost thoughts and motives. These expectations provide a powerful tool for potential harm or loss of dignity. Caution should be exercised if advice is sought where the investigator is not qualified to help. Even allowing a participant to pour out their heart, without offering advice, could lead to embarrassment and loss of dignity when they later discover that psychology does not, after all, mean therapy. The boundaries of expertise need to be very cautiously applied.

3.2 Informed consent

Investigations or interventions should not normally be carried out without the valid and informed consent of those taking part. Steps should be taken to ensure that the nature of the process, and any anticipated consequences, have been understood. Undue coercion should not take place through inappropriate financial inducement, or unequal positions of perceived power or status of those involved. In the case of patients, or those in care or in prison, it should be made clear that participation will in no way influence their future care or treatment prospects. Full disclosure of research procedures should generally occur. Information should only be withheld as part of a necessary aspect of the investigation, in which case information should be provided retrospectively. The rights of those with reduced or no capacity to give free informed consent, such as children, the elderly, those with learning disabilities, or those in care or in prison, should be specially safeguarded. In these cases, consent should instead be obtained from relevant others such as carers, guardians, close family members and/or those who have appropriate legal authority. In observational research, it is only deemed acceptable to proceed without prior consent in situations in which an individual might normally expect to be viewed by others, such as in a public space. Sample consent forms are provided in Box 1.4.

1.4

Three examples of consent forms

(A)   Informed consent form for an experiment with adult participants

Attentional Processes in Cigarette Smokers

I agree to take part in the above investigation. The purpose of the investigation has been explained to me, and I understand that confidentiality will be maintained at all times and that I can withdraw at any time.

The investigation will involve me taking part in a short test of reaction times on a computer, providing a sample of saliva and completing a questionnaire about my feelings.

☐ I have read the information sheet

☐ I have had the opportunity to ask questions and discuss the study

☐ I have received satisfactory answers to my questions

☐ I have received sufficient information about the study

☐ I am willing to take part in the study

Researcher
Signed   *Date*
....

Participant
Signed   *Date*
....
Name
....

Study approved by .... Ethics Committee

(B)   Parental consent form for an experiment with children

I have received the information leaflet explaining the nature of this study and my child's contribution to the research. By signing below I indicate that I give consent for my child to take part, and for any data I and my child provide to be used for research purposes. I understand that our contribution will remain completely anonymous and that I am free to withdraw my child, or my child's results, from this study at any time without giving a reason.

Child's name: (please print)..

Parent/guardian's name: (please print)...

Parent/guardian's signature:..............................date:..................

Please note: In order to maintain anonymity this consent form will be retained separately from any data that you or your child contributes

(C)   Consent form for an online research study

After an explanation of the nature of the task, including the time required to complete it online, the following consent section appeared, requiring a mouse click to continue:

> The nature and purpose of this study has been explained to me and by pressing the 'consent' button below I am giving my consent to take part. I understand any information that I provide will remain anonymous and that researchers will not be able to identify the contribution of any particular volunteer. I understand that I am free to withdraw from this study at any stage without giving reasons. I can simply close the browser window to abort my responses without any information being sent.

This study has been approved by the Open University Human Participants and Materials Ethical Committee (Ref: ....) and conforms to the ethics code of the British Psychological Society.

3.3   Withdrawal

Signing a consent form does not diminish the right that all participants have to withdraw from the research process at any stage. Indeed it is important that investigators make this clear from the outset and it is frequently a required clause within any consent form. Not only do participants have the right to terminate any session or agreement as they wish but they should retain their right to withdraw their own data, including such material as video/audio recordings, even retrospectively.

Participants might wish to withdraw for reasons ranging from distress to boredom, from misunderstanding of the requirements of the study to disdain for the potential outcomes of the research. Retrospective withdrawal of consent could arise, for example, when parents realize that an apparently innocent video of their small child snatching a toy from playmates was a precursor to serious bullying. If a child sadly dies or suffers serious illness, parents may find it distressing to think of researchers pouring over an early snapshot of their lives. Box 1.5 discusses other cases of withdrawal from research.

1.5

Withdrawal from research

When the nature and duration of a study is realistically explained to volunteers, it is rare for them to withdraw before completion. If the session is very nearly finished it might be reasonable to point this out to the withdrawing participant, but they should not be coerced into finishing the task. It is important to bear in mind that participants may not wish to explain the real reason for withdrawal, which could be quite unrelated to the tasks they are completing (they could be suffering from indigestion rather than objecting to the investigation).

Just as rare is the case where it may be necessary to withdraw the research from the participant (this problem is somewhat more likely to occur when payment is given for participation, attracting some recruits who are not primarily interested in helping with research). The following are examples of problems that could arise:

- The researcher could find themselves testing someone who swears and complains about the task and that this type (or all types) of psychological research is valueless.

- The participant may be very lonely and more interested in a friendly chat than concentrating on the task.

- The previous evening's, or the current day's, intake of drugs (alcohol or otherwise) may render the participant comatose in front of a less than exciting computer task, so they fall asleep.

Under such circumstances, a 'strategic retreat' is recommended – one that curtails the session without loss of dignity to the participant. The session could end early with only some tasks completed, or 'equipment failure' could terminate the session more abruptly. If payment was promised, then it should be given for the full amount of time that the participant expected to attend, regardless of how long the session actually lasts.

Withdrawal at a later date

Imagine that a parent has consented to their child being filmed as part of an observational study on pre-school cooperative play. During testing the child is possessive and has a tantrum which the parent finds a little embarrassing. Nevertheless, they agree that the researcher can use a video clip of their child as an example in illustrating their research findings in journal articles, talks and conference proceedings. A year or two later the same child is diagnosed with autism. Looking back to the earlier incident the parent is now anxious that the early signs were already visible. The thought of qualified psychologists pouring over such details of their child's early problems is upsetting to the parent who then withdraws consent for the researchers to make further use of the video clip.

3.4 Deception

Deception can take many forms. For instance, the following are all examples of deception of one kind or another:

- misleading participants about what their involvement will entail, either with respect to the nature of the tasks to be fulfilled, any discomfort they may feel, the time that they will take

- failing to acknowledge the nature or extent of any possible consequences of the study

- introducing confederates of the experimenter as if they are fellow participants or ordinary members of the public

- making dishonest claims about the value of the outcomes of the investigation.

Withholding of prior information about procedures may sometimes be justified when such knowledge would interfere with or invalidate the purpose of the investigation, but thorough debriefing is essential. On the whole, methods are not acceptable if participants are consistently left feeling they would have withdrawn or never taken part had the full procedure or true purpose been revealed earlier. Box 1.6 discusses a hypothetical case of deception.

1.6

Deception: is it acceptable to lie or mislead in the interests of science?

Box 1.1 provided you with a clear example of participants being misled about the nature of an experiment in which they agreed to take part. Below is a further example. You might consider whether you would find it acceptable if you were a member of an ethics committee and, if so, whether you would require any extra safeguards or procedures as a condition of your acceptance. As part of your considerations you need to think about whether the study could have been conducted equally successfully if fuller information about its true nature had been given beforehand.

Incidental learning

During a statistics lecture the lecturer made an excuse to his class of undergraduates and left the room, apparently to collect some handouts he had asked his secretary to copy. During his absence, two 'workmen' entered the lecture room, and unscrewed the whiteboard from the wall and removed it from the room. A 'porter' wearing distinctive uniform walked into the room during the procedure and walked behind the whiteboard. He rapidly reversed his jacket whilst behind the board and emerged wearing a different coloured uniform. He appeared to check some details with the two 'workmen' and they then all left the room. On his return, the maths lecturer explained that there had been a theft and handed out questionnaires asking the class to recall all they could about the incident. He asked everyone to put their name on the questionnaire and later the same day interviewed several students about their recollections, including questions aimed to determine whether they had noticed the change in uniform of the porter.

Note: Research has shown that it is quite likely that the students would not have noticed the change of clothes – indeed experiments suggest that the porter could have been substituted for another individual and even this gross change could have gone undetected.

ACTIVITY 1.3

Box 1.6 describes a study on incidental learning. As described, the study could not have taken place if students had been forewarned as to its purpose. But was this deception ethical? Take a few moments to consider whether the study was ethical, and how it might have been modified to circumvent ethical concerns.

COMMENT

Your consideration of this case may well generate more questions than answers. However, those questions can, in turn, help in deciding whether to grant ethical approval. Some questions that you might have considered are:

- Is it acceptable to deceive the students at all?
- How long can they be left thinking that a theft has taken place? Should they be debriefed immediately?
- Will belief that a theft has taken place under their very noses be distressing?
- Can the experimenter make use of these results without first getting the students to consent to having their data used this way?
- Would it be more acceptable if the class were psychology students for whom participation in such a study, and the time taken to do so, might be justified in terms of a learning experience?

3.5 Confidentiality and privacy

Information about research participants must be considered highly confidential, particularly if it includes anything of a sensitive nature. Data that include personal identifiers cannot be shared with other researchers without the consent of the participants. When research is disseminated it should not be possible to identify individual participants either directly or through the use of a thin disguise. Where it is necessary to retain personally identifiable information, where possible this should be held separately from other data which should be rendered anonymous as soon as possible. This is commonly achieved by providing individuals with an identity code. This code is used to distinguish participants' data, but the key to the code is held, along with any other necessary personal information, in a separate encrypted file.

Investigators should be careful not to divulge information obtained during sessions, even where this was not necessarily relevant to the research enterprise. If you recall from the discussion on competence in Section 3.1, some participants divulge all sorts of personal information thinking that this is relevant and/or appropriate. This privileged information should never be shared with others in a way that risks identifying the participant or anyone else that they mention (except in rare cases where there is danger of actual or potential harm to the participant or others). In the UK, specific rules associated with personal information are enshrined in the Data Protection Act (see Appendix), and equivalent legislation is in place in many other countries. Researchers need to be aware of current requirements surrounding storage and sharing of data. There are limited occasions when the breaking of confidentiality is not only acceptable but actually required by law. These are generally situations in which a participant divulges information about actual or intended criminal offences such as domestic violence or child abuse.

3.6 Risks

Investigators have a responsibility to ensure that taking part in their study will not expose participants to unnecessary risks that could have been anticipated. Of course, crossing the street or walking down stairs bring with them a small but recognizable risk of accident. What is deemed acceptable in a research setting is a degree of risk that a participant might expect to willingly encounter in their normal everyday, but not necessarily working, life. This distinction between working and everyday life is crucial of course, since those in the armed forces, for example, who may be regularly at risk, even of death, in the course of their duties, cannot expect a lesser standard of care in comparison with others when they freely volunteer in a research setting. Participants should not be coerced into taking risks that they would normally be reluctant to undertake, nor should they be induced to do so through the offer of financial reward. Participants must receive sufficient information to judge risks for themselves and be asked about factors that might make them vulnerable. Risks fall broadly into three categories: physical, emotional and social.

Potential physical risks are clearly paramount when using drugs or invasive or highly technical methods, such as electrophysiology or brain-imaging techniques, but basic health and safety issues must be considered in all situations. The testing environment as well as the equipment must be safe for its purpose. Physical risks can be created or exacerbated by pre-existing conditions, an issue that may be especially relevant if testing patients. Magnetic resonance imaging (MRI) techniques provide particularly emotive examples. Because of the very high strength of the magnetic field generated in this imaging technique, considerable force will be exerted on any metal substance in or on the body. As an example, MRI safety courses give dire warnings about walking into the scanning room carrying anything metal, say a hammer. Such items are liable to be snatched out of one's hand by the force of the magnetic field and travel at high speed towards the centre of the scanner and smash into it, and/or its occupant, causing potentially devastating damage and harm. Any metal lodged or implanted within the body of the potential participant, such as shrapnel, metal clips, valves or plates could be in danger of being dislodged, and any electronic device, such as a pacemaker or implanted hearing aid, may catastrophically malfunction. Clearly, researchers must be fully aware of these issues. Participants, and anyone else present, must be carefully screened and questioned, and any removable metal items set aside before they are allowed near the scanner.

Most procedures are far less risky, but still require routine precautions such as ensuring that electrical equipment is regularly tested for safety, that noise levels are not too high, that wires do not present a danger by trailing across floors, and so on. However, even sitting quietly at a computer screen can constitute a hazard for some. For instance, a rapidly flickering computer screen can impose risks for those vulnerable to epilepsy. It is up to the researcher to be as informed as possible about any likely problems.

Emotional risks are potentially always present, particularly when participants might be upset or feel humiliated when they find tasks difficult or tiring, especially as they are unlikely to realize that tests are often specifically devised to ensure relatively high error rates to avoid ceiling effects. But special care is required when testing involves deliberately manipulating emotions or includes vulnerable populations. For example, the elderly, highly anxious or depressed individuals, or patients with neurological damage (and particularly someone who is all of the above) may be especially sensitive to making errors, or become confused or react strongly to the use of emotional materials (see, for example, Box 1.3). Emotion research may necessitate using materials that are deliberately emotional such as pictures or videos showing threatening or distressing scenes, or may include inducing negative mood as part of a procedure (see, for example, **Yiend and Macintosh, 2010**). Emotional risks may also follow if cultural or religious values are violated, or if participants feel they, or their gender, sexual orientation, racial or religious affiliations are being demeaned or discriminated against by the process or materials used in the investigation. It is not always easy to anticipate what might raise concerns for participants, and investigators may need to seek advice. When these types of risk are inherent in the research, it is particularly important that potential recruits to the study are fully informed of the nature of the study and the materials at or before the stage at which they consent to participate. It is also vital that procedures are in place to deal sympathetically and appropriately with any distress that might arise (see Section 3.8 on debriefing).

Social risks are often hard to define and can be quite subtle, but could include encouraging, or potentially creating, discriminatory attitudes or behaviour by appearing to provide support for these attitudes in the materials used or the behaviour of investigators or their collaborators.

3.7 Recruitment and payment

Recruitment and initial contact with potential participants should follow the same guidelines as the research process itself. That is, any message conveyed during the recruitment procedure should provide honest information about what is expected and should not make exaggerated claims for the effectiveness of the research (or products, if any, to be tested). Some research requires participants to have particular characteristics, such as being within a specified age range or educational background, being bilingual, having English as a first language, or having a history of specific physical or emotional disorder. In these cases investigators should seek neither to cause offence, upset or alienation of any particular group nor to inadvertently give negative labels to target groups.

Payment for time and expense should not be offered in such a way as to coerce potential participants into taking greater risks than they might otherwise agree to within their normal lifestyle. Some ethics committees do not think it appropriate to pay participants who have been recruited because they have particular medical conditions, since this is seen to constitute inappropriate pressure to take part.

3.8 Debriefing

In all studies, participants should expect to receive some general information about the study to which they are contributing and its purpose. Where deception or an unexpected aspect of the procedure was involved this should be explained and reasons for the deception or withholding of information justified. In cases where there may be specific risks, the debriefing procedures should be carefully thought out. For instance, some experiments in emotion research include procedures intended to induce either a negative or positive mood during the session. It is important to check that participants' moods have returned to pre-experiment levels, and if necessary use procedures to repair mood before they leave. The most obvious danger is that a negative mood will persist, causing distress and disruption, but it is possible to imagine that inducing an overly positive mood could present just as great a problem. For instance, leaving the testing session with 'not a care in the world' could be a danger if it encouraged rash or risky behaviour. A euphoric individual could feel invincible, or convinced that this was their lucky day for a hefty bet at the races, or a purchase on the stock market. Debriefing and especially mood repair may require time that should be allowed for in the testing schedule. Additionally, it may necessitate organizing back-up from clinically qualified personnel or providing information directing participants towards professional help. The particular requirements of the debriefing period should be part of the risk assessment for the study. Investigators should attempt to anticipate problems that might arise due to their research intervention and make contingency plans to take account of them. Participants, and if necessary their relatives or carers, should be given a route to contact the investigator or their team if problems should persist or arise some time after the testing session.

3.9   Feedback and conveying specialist information

Debriefing about the purpose and significance of the research project is a separate issue from giving feedback to participants about their individual level of performance or scores on tests and questionnaires. Where, for instance, children's developmental milestones are estimated, or IQ or personality tests or questionnaires measuring emotional vulnerability are given, caution should be exercised about whether feedback should be provided, and if so how. In many cases it is best to withhold detailed feedback to avoid the information being misused or misinterpreted. However, it is often desirable to explain why this will be the case, or the investigator could (with honesty) indicate that not enough is known about the tests to be able to make a valid comparison with the scores of other people. In brain-imaging procedures, consideration should be given as to how to proceed if a scan should reveal abnormalities, such as brain tumours, about which the participant was not previously aware, or deterioration of an existing condition beyond that expected.

3.10   Colleagues and students

It is an investigator's responsibility to ensure that any assistants, students or colleagues working with them on a project also adhere to the appropriate ethical guidelines. They should encourage fellow researchers to follow ethical guidelines and bring the guidelines to their attention if they consider that they are not doing so.

3.11   The safety of the researcher

The sections above concentrate mainly on the experience of the participant in research. However, the safety and well-being of the researcher themselves must be an additional focus of attention. Although often falling within the more general remit of 'health and safety at work', the researcher's own well-being must not be overlooked. This will include their response to the research situation or materials, the reaction to participants' responses, or the risks associated with testing participants alone outside working hours or in the participant's own home.

3.12   Personal conduct

It is imperative that investigators ensure that their research procedures are ethically sound and this includes how they themselves behave towards all those they contact in the course of their research. They must conduct themselves in a professional manner that in no way takes advantage of their privileged position in terms of access, status or presumed power over their participants (or participants' relatives, carers and so on). This includes being polite, punctual and considerate in their dealings, and refraining from any practices that might impair their ability or professional judgement (such as taking drugs or alcohol). Hopefully, it goes without saying that those undertaking research should never exploit the research setting for financial or political advantage nor gratification of personal desires.

3.13   Internet-mediated research

Increasing use of the Internet as a tool for research opens new areas of ethical consideration. Most, if not all, of the issues discussed in this chapter still apply when researchers contact their participants over the Internet. It is often only the format that must change. However, new issues are created by the absence of direct contact between investigator and participant. This can be highly relevant to the outcome of the research enterprise as there can be no control over the circumstances prevailing whilst the study takes place. The researcher cannot be sure who is participating, or whether they are providing honest information about themselves. This merely exaggerates an existing problem in human participant research, but in face-to-face contact it is usual to be able to verify at least the sex of the participant and their approximate age. Even the accuracy of these simple statistics cannot be assumed over the Internet. There are separate methodological issues also. It is up to the researcher, for instance, to arrange (or attempt to arrange) to debar repeat attempts by the same participant, or a group of friends contributing together. Special techniques may be required to compensate for the lack of the experimenter. For instance, to thwart obvious cheating in a memory experiment, the online 'back' button may need to be effectively deactivated or bypassed to prevent a return to the 'to be remembered' material once recall is required. These are essentially practical rather than ethical issues.

From an ethical standpoint, as with all research formats, it is important that the participant is properly informed about the nature of the study, including how long it will take; that they understand they are free to withdraw and that their information is held confidentially (and preferably anonymously); and that they are offered information and debriefing at the end of the study. After receiving the relevant information, consent must be sought by a device such as clicking on a 'consent' button (see Box 1.4(C)). Because researchers cannot be sure of the age of any potential participants, they need to be cautious about the material presented. In the absence of the investigator in person, some mode of contact should be provided, usually an email address, in case worries or concerns arise from the research. Harvesting information from newsgroups and web pages requires care over confidentiality, and infiltrating discussion groups and 'seeding' them with the investigator's own information raises the usual issues of deceit and manipulation that arise in many non-Internet studies. These issues are, to some extent, variations on themes that arise when questioning the ethics of observing people in public places without their consent, or when researchers act as participant observers and their own behaviour alters that of the group.

Internet methods allow interesting alternatives on the theme of deception. For instance, because there is no personal contact it is a simple matter to investigate the influence of the apparent sex/race/religion/disability, etc. of the investigator merely by adapting the text or providing (misleading) pictorial information. Of course, the participant may suspect the deception and, in any case, ease of deception means that the honesty of the respondent can be equally suspect! However, there is some evidence that the anonymity of the computer, in comparison with an investigator present in person, is helpful when completing sensitive questionnaires. Participants may be prepared to reveal more personal information via a computer keyboard than with pencil-and-paper methods.

Box 1.7 discusses the related issue of ethical considerations in relation to the media, and specifically in connection with 'reality' TV programmes.

1.7

Ethics and the media: anything goes?

Not uncommonly, researchers and students alike will complain that the ethical codes that constrain research seem to go out of the window when the media are involved, when public entertainment or public 'information' are the criteria rather than scientific endeavour. Invasion of privacy, intrusion, embarrassment, loss of dignity, deliberate distress or humiliation are not uncommon, and whilst some of these are entered into with willing consent (perhaps aided by the promise of fame or financial coercion), many are not.

A well-known social psychology experiment by Zimbardo (1975, 1999) was recreated for a television series in which recruits took the part of 'prisoners' or 'guards' and lived in a specially created set. This is not unusual and there have been many 'reality' TV shows requiring participants to live on set, to obey strict rules of conduct, to complete tasks and challenges that have not been explained in advance, to be constantly on camera and to be denied contact with their family and friends. It would be extremely unlikely that these procedures would be accepted by a research ethics panel, yet there are panels that consider the ethics of TV productions and these programmes must have been scrutinized. This is not, by any means, the only area where such an obvious double standard applies. In the ethics of animal welfare, the rules applied to the care and conditions of animals maintained for research insist on standards (space per animal, temperature regulation, cleanliness, air conditions and so on) that far exceed those of farm animals maintained for food. You may consider whether it is appropriate that ethical rules differ depending on whether science, entertainment or food is the aim. However, these contrasts merely serve to highlight the many inconsistencies in all human activities. Ethical considerations change with context, culture and time; one thing we can be fairly sure about is that the debate about what is appropriate in research, and elsewhere, is not about to end soon.

ACTIVITY 1.4

Consider a 'reality' TV programme with which you have some familiarity. How well does the programme stand up to ethical scrutiny? For each of the main issues discussed in Section 3, try to decide whether the programme deals with the issue satisfactorily. If you are unsure, think about what further information you would need.

Summary of Section 3

- Before embarking on research at any level, researchers must ensure that their proposed research will satisfy appropriate ethical guidelines, concerning at least the following issues:
  - competence
  - consent
  - withdrawal
  - deception
  - confidentiality and privacy
  - risks
  - recruitment and payment
  - debriefing
  - feedback and conveying specialist information
  - colleagues and students
  - the safety of the researcher
  - personal conduct.
- Internet-mediated research raises additional practical and ethical questions.

4   Special cases

Whilst the sections above should apply equally to all studies, it is worth highlighting the kinds of special issues that might be particularly relevant to some of the studies mentioned in this and its companion volume. This helps to increase awareness of the types of issues that might arise in any investigation.

4.1   Work with patients

Ethical issues surrounding work with patients begin well before they are even invited to participate in research. Procedures for identifying those who might fulfil the criteria for inclusion in a study, and then making initial contact with them, must not breach the confidentiality of the medical records held by health professionals. Once contact has been made, are patients able to give informed consent to help with the research? If not, who will act in their best interests and make a decision on their behalf? Is it possible to research brainwave sensitivity in coma patients, for instance, if no relatives are visiting who might provide consent? Special care must be taken not to exacerbate patients' condition, overtax their ability, humiliate them, nor insensitively bring to their attention deficiencies or abnormalities of which they were previously unaware. Patients who agree to help with research should not be 'over tested' by a whole series of researchers. Thus researchers and their colleagues must seek to make arrangements to space out testing sessions to avoid exploitation. Special consideration and respect need to be given to those caring for these patients. See Box 1.8 for further discussion of such issues.

1.8

Exploitation or valuable contribution? The use of patients in research

Most psychologists have heard of HM (Henry Molaison 1926–2008) whose memory problems are almost invariably reported in introductory texts (see **Rutherford, 2010**). Consider the ethics of having asked HM to take part in a research project. He would not have remembered who you were even if you had met previously. He would not remember any previous testing sessions. Within a short time of describing the procedures he would have forgotten you even mentioned them. How could he give consent? If someone gave consent on his behalf, were they allowing researchers to exploit his disability in a way that is demeaning? What alternative activities would have occupied his time if researchers were denied the opportunities to include him in their research? Was his quality of life (or that of those who cared for him) enhanced or diminished by his contribution? There are no straightforward answers to these questions. HM contributed many hours of his time in the interests of research and without doubt his contribution has been very valuable. There are a number of other patients who are 'in demand' for research purposes; some are too handicapped by their disability to take up normal paid employment, but many seem to enjoy taking part and the interest shown in them; they often build up strong personal relationships or friendships with researchers for whom they give very generously of their time.

Patients who are sufficiently rehabilitated (or working towards this) to have gained some independence may be held back if testing sessions take up their valuable time, or leave them too tired to cope with their own everyday tasks. On the other hand, sometimes carers welcome the arrival of a researcher, who will 'occupy' their 'charge' for a time, or at least provide someone with whom a normal conversation can take place, and a break in an otherwise constrained routine. Each case must be treated as unique, and the pros and cons of contributing to research assessed for all those involved. When 'one more patient with frontal lobe damage' is required for a project, it is important not to take advantage of their goodwill and coerce the patient or family into taking part when this may be disruptive to their routine or harmful to their well-being.

4.2   Brain imaging

Participants in either PET (positron emission tomograpy) scanning or MRI (magnetic resonance imaging) must be screened before they participate. Potentially intrusive questions must be asked and researchers need to exercise sensitivity whilst doing so even though the process may be routine from their standpoint. For instance, for PET scanning, only women beyond the menopause can take part since exposure to even the minute doses of radioactive substances used might constitute a risk for an unborn foetus. Women may be embarrassed or insulted if asked for this information insensitively. Likewise, screening questions that are used before MRI procedures can take place involve asking about previous brain and other operations, the presence of clips or metal fittings in the body, pacemakers, the possible presence of shrapnel and the possession of tattoos (which apparently contain metal). The scanning experience itself can be lengthy and the participant has to remain very still for quite long periods. PET involves injection of radioactive substances, whilst the MRI scan involves potentially claustrophobic confinement within the bore of the apparatus and when scanning is taking place the machine is very noisy. Participants may find these conditions unacceptable, particularly if they have an anxious disposition (see Chapter 2 for more details of these techniques).

4.3   Emotion research

Some of the sections above have considered a few of the special issues that become relevant when researchers work with individuals who are within or close to the clinical range for emotional disorders, such as anxiety and depression. Special care has to be taken that the testing situation itself is neither unduly upsetting nor likely to trigger an emotional episode after the event. When emotional material is presented, participants need to be warned ahead, and sufficiently early in the recruitment process that they feel able to withdraw without guilt or embarrassment. It is good practice to show them examples before they begin if the material is extreme. Participants need to be fully warned if they are to be asked about their feelings during the course of the study. They should not be made to feel belittled or vulnerable by being overtly categorized as falling within a particular emotional grouping (e.g. by being labelled as 'high in neuroticism' or 'depressed'). Procedures may need to be put into place to ensure that the participant's mood has returned to normal at the end of the session and that contact details are provided in case problems arise later. Researchers themselves may need to be given special support if they habitually deal with participants who become upset during the course of investigations.

4.4   Researching with children

The ethical issues discussed in this chapter raise special problems when conducting research with children. In particular, the researcher needs to acknowledge the power relationships that exist between adults and children. In many societies, adults teach and children learn. In a sense, in conducting research with children, the researcher reverses this relationship by asking the children to share their experiences, and tell the researcher what they think. Child participants are entitled to the same sort of respect as adult participants. This means the researcher must gain consent, respect anonymity, maintain the right to withdraw and give feedback. It can be difficult to achieve informed consent with younger children. For example, how do you explain what might be complex research aims? Can children appreciate what it means to agree to take part in a research study? It is difficult to provide general answers to these questions because how the study is explained will depend on the child and the situation. In any event, the researcher must get the consent of the child's parent or guardian and, if at all possible, the consent of the child her/himself. They should also be sensitive to the child's behaviour during the research. It may be that because of the power relationships referred to above the child does not say that s/he is experiencing distress. The researcher will need to be vigilant and, if the child is uncomfortable, bring the activity to a close. Again, in giving feedback about the research, both the child and the parent must be treated with respect.

Summary of Section 4

- Particular kinds of research study raise special ethical questions. These include:
  - work with patients
  - brain-imaging studies
  - emotion research
  - research with children.

5 Conclusion

Ethical issues involve complex and evolving considerations that attempt to protect the well-being of research participants, and the reputation of institutions and the discipline and professions of psychology and the neurosciences. Ethical decisions are frequently difficult and involve weighing up both the procedures proposed and the potential benefit of the research outcomes to others. Research in psychology and the neurosciences is governed by sets of guidelines designed to ensure that participants in research do not emerge from the research experience harmed physically, emotionally or financially by their participation. On the contrary it is hoped that they will feel appreciated, informed and have a positive attitude towards the research enterprise to which they have contributed, towards the institution where it took place and towards psychology and the neurosciences as professions. It is up to all who are involved in research to attempt to further this aim.

Further reading

Ethical codes are frequently updated, so you may wish to search for and consult sources on the Internet. However, the following general texts provide further exploration of some of the issues raised in this chapter.

Bersoff, D.N. (ed.) (2003) *Ethical Conflicts in Psychology* (3rd edn), Washington, DC, American Psychological Association.

Nagy, T.F. (1999) *Ethics in Plain English: An Illustrative Casebook for Psychologists*, Washington, DC, American Psychological Association.

Sales, B.D. and Folkman, S. (eds) (2000) *Ethics in Research With Human Participants*, Washington, DC, American Psychological Association.

References

Milgram, S. (1963) 'Behavioural study of obedience', *Journal of Abnormal and Social Psychology*, vol.67, pp.371–8.

Milgram, S. (1974) *Obedience to Authority*, London, Tavistock.

Rutherford, A. (2010) 'Long-term memory: encoding to retrieval' in Kaye, H. (ed.) *Cognitive Psychology* (2nd edn), Milton Keynes, The Open University.

Yiend, J. and Mackintosh, B. (2010) 'Cognition and emotion' in Kaye, H. (ed.) *Cognitive Psychology* (2nd edn), Milton Keynes, The Open University.

Zimbardo, P.G. (1975) 'Transforming experimental research into advocacy of social change', in Deutsch, M. and Hornstein, H. (eds) *Applying Social Psychology*, Hillsdale, NJ, Lawrence Erlbaum.

Zimbardo, P.G. (1999) *Stanford Prison Experiment: A Simulation Study of the Psychology of Imprisonment Conducted at Stanford University*, http://www.prisonexp.org (accessed 25 October 2010).

Neuroimaging: techniques for examining human brain function

Ingrid S. Johnsrude and Olaf Hauk

1   Introduction

Fifty years ago, almost the only way to relate human behaviour and cognition to the function of parts of the brain was to look for specific deficits in patients with damage confined to a particular region of the brain (acquired through, for example, stroke, injury, or surgery for neurological disease). Identifying the location of brain damage would often have to wait until after the patient's death, since the only way to examine brain structure in living people was the **pneumoencephalogram**, a low-resolution, poor-contrast X-ray that was neither painless nor harmless.

Figure 2.1   A magnetic resonance image of the brain of a neurologically normal individual. With fine spatial resolution, different brain structures can be easily identified: here, the image reveals different tissues such as grey matter (dark grey), white matter (light grey), fat (white) and fluid (black). Similarly, anatomical abnormalities can be identified, delineated, and localized with a high degree of accuracy

Although studies of brain-damaged people (neuropsychology – see Chapter 3) remain extremely valuable, the development of functional imaging techniques has had an enormous impact on the way we assess human cognition. Detailed anatomical images, acquired through techniques such as computerized tomography (CT) and magnetic resonance imaging (MRI), can now be used to identify structure in normal individuals (as shown in Figure 2.1) and localize damage in patients. Furthermore, detailed anatomical images from normal volunteers and patients can be combined with functional information from positron emission tomography (PET), functional magnetic resonance imaging (fMRI), electroencephalography (EEG) and magnetoencephalography (MEG) to explore normal and abnormal brain function.

Most neuroimaging techniques are easy and painless for volunteers. MEG (shown in Figure 2.2(a)) involves sitting in a device that looks rather like an old-fashioned beauty-salon hairdryer. Inside the headpiece are sensitive devices for measuring the magnetic fields produced by the brain (see Section 2.1.4). EEG (Figure 2.2(b)) involves putting electrodes, sensitive to the aggregate activity of large numbers of neurons, on the scalp with a conductive gel. Often, as is shown here, the electrodes are incorporated into a cap, which makes setting up the electrode array less time-consuming. Activation PET (Figure 2.2(c)) involves the volunteer lying comfortably on a bed with an IV (intravenous drip) in one arm; a small amount of radioactively labelled water is periodically injected via the IV prior to each scan. In fMRI (Figure 2.2(d) and (e)), as in PET, the volunteer is lying comfortably on a bed which slides into the scanner.

Transcranial magnetic stimulation (TMS), if used within safety limits, can safely and temporarily disrupt function in a specific brain region, essentially producing a temporary 'lesion', in order to evaluate the importance of that area of the brain to performance on a given task. All of these tools are powerful additions to the traditional neuropsychological method of cataloguing deficits in patients, as ways to understand the relationship between brain and behaviour.

Each neuroimaging technique has its own advantages and disadvantages, many of which come under the general heading of **resolution**. The resolution of a technique indicates how far away, in space or time, two events have to be before they can be distinguished as two separate events. For example, EEG and MEG, which measure the electrical (EEG) or magnetic (MEG) fields generated by the activity of groups of neurons, have very good **temporal resolution** (in the order of milliseconds). This means that two events happening very quickly one after the other can be distinguished. However, as will be explained in the next section, the **spatial resolution** of EEG and MEG is only in the range of several centimetres, and the techniques are not equally sensitive over the whole brain. This means that EEG and MEG data cannot be linked to a particular region of the brain with much confidence. PET and fMRI are sensitive to the brain's metabolism (of oxygen in particular) and can be used to localize active tissue with great precision, but their temporal resolution is quite poor (a few hundred milliseconds at best, for the most sophisticated experimental fMRI designs) (see Plate 1 in the colour plates section).

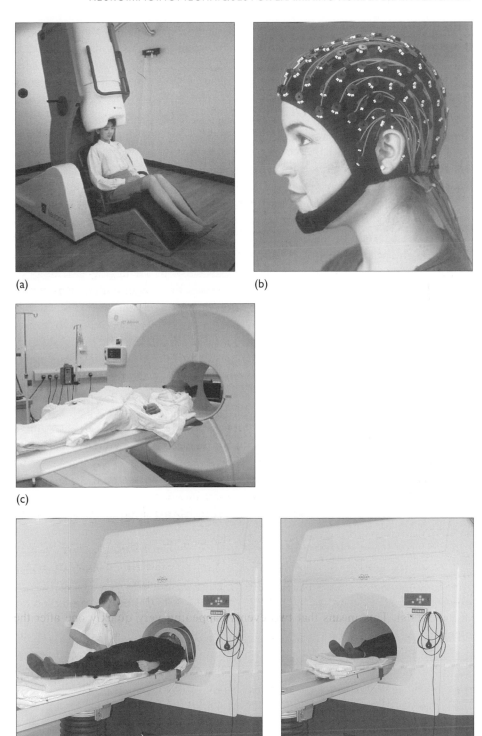

(a)

(b)

(c)

(d)

(e)

Figure 2.2   (a) MEG, (b) EEG, (c) Activation PET, (d and e) fMRI

These tools each have their own special place in answering questions about cognition. If a question concerns 'where' in the brain a certain process occurs, then either PET or fMRI would be helpful. Recent fMRI studies, for example, have shown that different parts of the ventral visual processing pathway in the temporal-occipital cortex are specialized for processing different kinds of things such as faces (and other parts of the body), places, and tools. If, however, the question concerns 'when' a process occurs or the order in which different brain areas (identified perhaps using PET or fMRI) become active, then EEG and MEG can be helpful. For example, both EEG and MEG can be used to show that, when a word is heard, frontal and temporal areas known to be important for language become active *after* auditory cortex does. Unlike the other methods, both TMS and the lesion method (the classic neuropsychological method of assessing the cognitive function of patients with focal brain lesions) reveal whether a particular brain area is *necessary* for a particular function, not just whether it is *involved* when a task tapping that function is performed.

This chapter introduces these various techniques, the assumptions underlying the methods, how they work, and what their advantages, disadvantages and limitations are. We review how experiments using these techniques are designed to ask cognitive and neuroscientific questions, how data are analysed, and how results are interpreted. We begin by presenting methods based on measuring the brain's electrical activity (EEG/MEG), then present methods based on brain metabolism (PET/SPECT/fMRI), and then briefly present transcranial magnetic stimulation (TMS) as a tool for inducing 'reversible lesions'. The information presented here should help you to understand papers on topics in cognitive psychology or cognitive neuroscience. It may also help you to begin to think creatively about how particular questions regarding the relationship between brain and behaviour might best be addressed.

2 EEG and MEG: measuring the timing of electrical activity in the brain

The electrical activity of nerve cells (neurons) in the brain produces currents spreading through the head. These currents, representing the integrated activity of many thousands of neurons, also reach the scalp surface. The resulting voltage differences on the scalp can be recorded as the **electroencephalogram (EEG)**. The currents inside the head produce magnetic fields, which can also be measured above the scalp surface as the **magnetoencephalogram (MEG)**. EEG and MEG reflect brain electrical activity with millisecond temporal resolution, and provide the most direct measure correlate of ongoing brain processing that can be obtained non-invasively (without physically entering the body).

2.1 Collecting data

2.1.1 EEG sampling

The **continuous** or **spontaneous EEG** (i.e. voltage fluctuations as a function of time, which can be viewed directly for each electrode during the recording – see Plate 2(a) in the colour plates section) can be clinically very helpful. For example, it can be used to diagnose epilepsy or another seizure disorder, predict seizures, detect abnormal brain states or classify sleep stages.

However, the amplitude of the continuous EEG signal is of the order of several tens of microvolts (μV), i.e. about a million times weaker than that of household batteries. It therefore requires special amplifiers that amplify the signal and convert it to a digital signal that can be stored and processed on a computer. Recordings are taken virtually simultaneously at all recording sites (several tens to several hundreds) and at different time points (usually every few milliseconds). The time difference between sampling points is called the **sampling interval**. The **sampling rate** is given by the number of samples per second, i.e.

$$\frac{1{,}000 \text{ ms}}{(\text{sampling interval in ms})}.$$

In typical EEG or MEG studies, a sampling rate of 200–500 Hertz (Hz) is common (corresponding to sampling intervals of between 5 and 2 ms).

2.1.2 EEG electrodes

Both EEG and MEG are recorded using a system of electrodes or sensors placed on or above the scalp. Electrodes are usually little metal disks that are pasted onto the scalp among the hair. They are either mounted on a cap (e.g. if a large number of electrodes is used), or can be fixed one by one. To assure good data quality, a conductive substance usually has to be inserted between the electrodes and the scalp to improve the contact between the two. A particular advantage of EEG compared to MEG, fMRI and PET is that once the electrodes are fitted the participant is allowed to move the head within certain limits. This makes this technique suitable for infants or for patient groups where head movement cannot be restricted.

To compare results across different studies, electrode locations must be standardized and locations need to be easily determined for individual subjects. Common is the so-called **extended 10/20 system**, where electrode locations are defined with respect to fractions of the distance between **nasion** and **inion** (i.e. root of the nose to 'the little bump on the back of your head', or 'front-back') and the **pre-auricular points** (the little skin lobules in front of your ear canals, or 'left-right'). Electrode labels like 'FPz' or 'PO4' indicate the area of the head ('Fronto-Polar', 'Parieto-Occipital'), odd numbers mark left- and even numbers mark right-hemispheric locations, and the lower the number, the nearer the electrode is to the mid-line ('z' indicates a location on the mid-line). 'TP8' ('Temporo-Parietal') is therefore more to the right than 'TP2', and 'F5' ('Frontal') is more to the left than 'F1'.

2.1.3 Referencing in EEG

Electric potentials are only defined with respect to a reference, i.e. an arbitrarily chosen 'zero level'. The choice of the reference may differ depending on the purpose of the recording. This is similar to measures of height, where the zero level can be at sea level if we refer to the height of mountains, or at ground level if we refer to the height of a building, or floor level for the height of a person.

For each EEG recording, a **reference electrode** has to be selected in advance. Ideally, this electrode would be affected by global voltage changes (e.g. slow voltage shifts due to perspiration) in the same manner as all the other electrodes, such that brain non-specific activity is subtracted out by the referencing. Also, the reference should not pick up signals that are not intended to be recorded, like heart activity, which would be 'subtracted in' by the referencing. Possible locations for reference electrodes are the ear lobes, the tip of the nose, or the mastoids (i.e. the bones behind the ears). With multi-channel recordings (e.g. more than 32 channels), instead of having a single, separate reference electrode, average activity across all channels is used as a reference. In other words, it is common to compute the **average reference**, i.e. to subtract the average across all electrodes from each electrode for each time point. Even if a single reference electrode was used during the recording, it is always possible to reference the data to any of the recording electrodes (or combinations of them, like their average) at a later stage of processing.

2.1.4 MEG recordings

The magnetic field, in contrast to the electric potential, has a direction, usually illustrated by magnetic field lines. The strength of the magnetic fields produced by the human brain is less than a millionth of the earth's magnetic field. Such small field strengths can be measured by so-called **superconducting quantum interference devices** (SQUIDs). Because MEG sensors are so very sensitive, they have to be well shielded against magnetic noise. The shielding of the laboratory and the SQUID technology make an MEG device 10 to 100 times more expensive than an EEG system, and the required permanent helium-cooling (required for the super-conductivity of the detectors) imposes considerable maintenance costs.

A special and important feature of MEG is its sensitivity to the topography of the brain – the details of the structure of its surface. The brain surface is quite dramatically folded, and whether the MEG signal arises in the convex tops of the folds (gyri) or the concave depths of the folds (sulci) affects sensitivity to neuronal current sources (**dipoles**). MEG is particularly insensitive to **radial dipoles**, those directed towards or away from the scalp (like at the top of a gyrus). It mainly 'sees' **tangential dipoles**, which are parallel to the scalp. The full explanation for this characteristic would involve a fair amount of physics and mathematics. A special case of a radial dipole is a dipole located at the centre of a sphere: it must necessarily point away from the centre, and is therefore radial and 'invisible' for MEG. Roughly speaking, the nearer a source is to the centre, 'the more radial' it is. This implies that the deeper a source is in the head, the less visible it is for MEG. This seems to be a disadvantage for MEG, but turns into an advantage if superficial and tangential sources (e.g. in sulci of the cortex) are targeted, since in that case the corresponding MEG signal is less contaminated than EEG by other possibly disturbing sources. Furthermore, it has been shown that superficial and tangential sources can be localized with more accuracy than with EEG, particular in somatosensory and some auditory parts of the brain. MEG has therefore been widely used to study early acoustic and phonetic processing, and the plasticity of the somatosensory and auditory system.

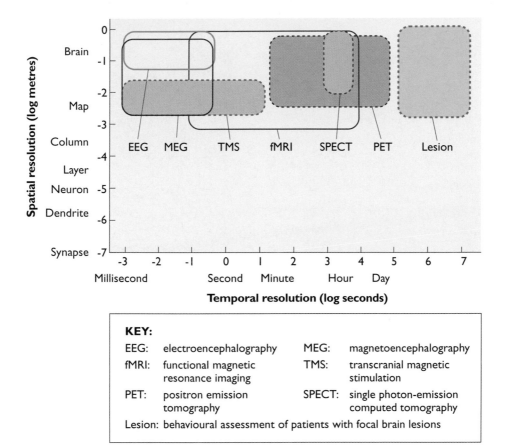

KEY:

EEG:	electroencephalography	MEG:	magnetoencephalography
fMRI:	functional magnetic resonance imaging	TMS:	transcranial magnetic stimulation
PET:	positron emission tomography	SPECT:	single photon-emission computed tomography
Lesion:	behavioural assessment of patients with focal brain lesions		

Plate 1   The ranges of temporal and spatial resolution of methods used to study human brain function, based on performance with typical hardware and commonly used experimental protocols. Shading indicates invasive techniques. The vertical axis includes references to 'maps' (e.g. visual or motor maps of space and the body); 'columns' (which are functionally specialized regions within a particular brain region – e.g. orientation columns in the visual cortex contain neurons which all fire when viewing a line that is angled a particular way); and 'layers' (the cortex of the brain is composed of six layers)

Source: adapted from Cohen and Bookheimer, 1994; Churchland and Sejnowski, 1988

(a) Continuous EEG

(b) Averaged EEG

(c) Time plot of ERP ('ERP curves')

(d) Topography of ERP at 90 ms

Plate 2   Data pre-processing of event-related EEG and MEG data:
(a) Illustration of the averaging procedure used in standard ERP analysis
(b) Averages consisting of 1, 10 and 80 time segments, respectively. Note that the pre-stimulus interval ('baseline') flattens with increasing number of segments, while the event-related response becomes less distorted by noise, i.e. the 'signal-to-noise ratio' (SNR) increases
(c) The averaged curves can be plotted for each electrode or sensor location separately. Channels are plotted according to their relative position on the head
(d) A continuous topographic plot over the head. Red colour indicates positive and blue colour negative signals. The picture shows the event-related potential topography 90 ms after visual presentation of a word, with two distinct positive peaks over left and right occipital scalp areas, presumably reflecting processing of visual stimulus features

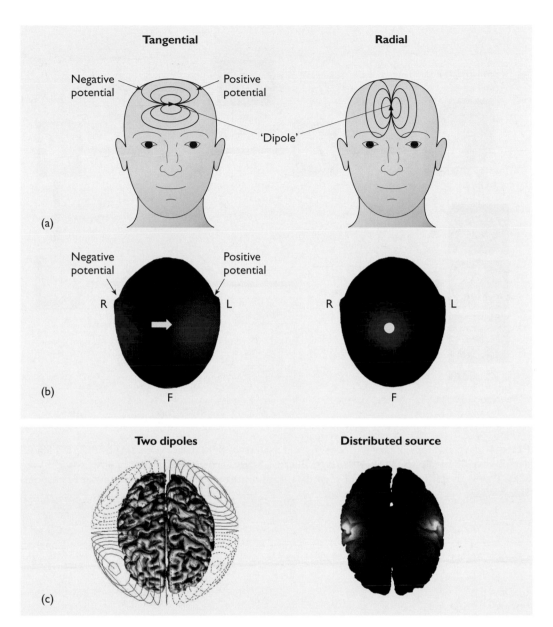

Plate 3 The generation and modelling of EEG/MEG signals:

(a) The summed electrical activity within a small area of cortex can be described by a so called 'dipole'. This dipole describes the strength and direction of the current flow within this area. Each dipole has a positive scalp potential in the direction in which it points, and a negative potential in the opposite direction

(b) (*left*) Potential distribution for a tangential dipole (pointing right-to-left), and (*right*) potential distribution for a radial dipole (pointing downwards). The magnetic field of a tangential dipole is roughly perpendicular to its potential distribution (not shown)

(c) Illustration of the 'inverse problem' in EEG/MEG analysis: the images both represent different ways in which the same surface electrical and magnetic activity could be produced

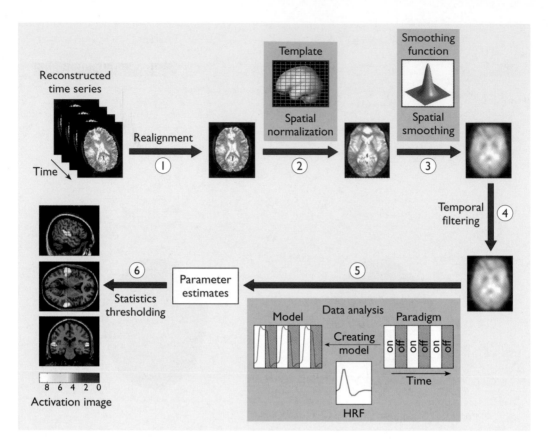

Plate 4 Typical steps of image processing and analysis of fMRI data. Processing of PET and SPECT data is very similar up to the analysis stage. Because images are not acquired as quickly with PET and SPECT as with fMRI, the analysis of such data does not need to take the haemodynamic response function (see Section 3.4.1) into account

Plate 5 Standardized stereotaxic coordinate system, with perpendicular x-, y- and z-axes (see (a) and (b)). The star in (c) is in the location (x,y,z) −45, +15, +10. This is approximately 4.5 cm left of the midline, 1.5 cm in front of the anterior commissure, and 1 cm above the AC–PC line. This point always falls in the left inferior frontal gyrus in normalized brains

Plate 6 Transcranial magnetic stimulation (TMS). With the head fixed in position, a wire coil is placed over the scalp and skull. A strong magnetic field is induced by current flowing in the coil, and this field penetrates into a focal area of cortex. This causes a disruption of neural activity in the affected region

Source: George, 2003, p.69

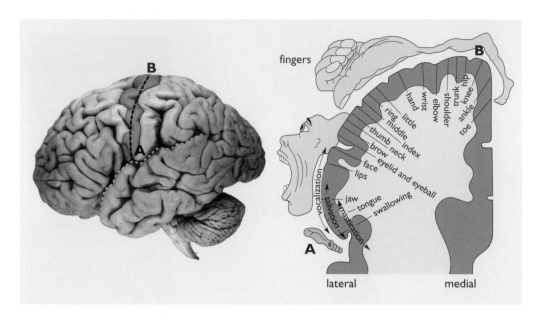

Plate 7 The 'motor homunculus'. The primary motor region (A–B) represents different parts of the body in an orderly way. The part of the motor cortex involved in mouth and tongue movements (and so in speech production) is found at the lower end, near the Sylvian fissure (blue dotted line)

Plate 8 This computerized image of Phineas Gage's skull shows the path that the tamping iron followed through his skull

Source: Damasio et al., 1994

Plate 9 Lesion location for participants with impaired recognition for different kinds of category: (A) Impaired recognition of unique persons. The surface overlap (left half of panel) is shown in the inferior view (leftmost), and in the right lateral (upper) and mesial views (lower) of the normal brain. The lines on the lateral and mesial views indicate the position of the four coronal slices seen in the right half of the panel. In the coronal cuts, the extent of lesion overlap into white matter can be appreciated (B) Impaired recognition of animals. In the left half of the panel, the surface overlap can be seen in the inferior and mesial views of the right and left hemispheres. The four coronal slices in the right half of the panel show the depth overlap (C) Impaired recognition of tools. The surface overlap is shown in the lateral view of the left hemisphere, and the depth overlap is shown in the three coronal slices (D) Colour bar indicating the number of participants contributing to the overlaps

Source: Tranel et al., 1997

2.2   Computing event-related potentials (ERPs) and event-related fields (ERFs)

Whereas the continuous EEG can be useful clinically, the use of EEG and MEG to investigate more specific perceptual or cognitive processes requires more sophisticated data processing than just recording electrical signals through the arrays of electrodes on the head. Usually, the electrical signals resulting from a particular cognitive event (e.g. hearing a word) are averaged over many trials (see colour Plate 2(b)), a method that assumes the brain response does not markedly change its timing or spatial distribution during the experiment.

Data are divided into time segments (**trials** or **epochs**) of fixed length (e.g. one second), where the time point zero is usually defined as the onset of the stimulus. These time segments can then be averaged either across all stimuli present in the study, or for subgroups of stimuli that are to be compared with each other. Doing so, any random fluctuations should cancel each other out, since they might have positive amplitudes in one segment, but negative amplitudes in another. In contrast, any brain response that is time-locked to the presentation of the stimulus will add up constructively and be reflected in the average activity across trials. These averaged data are usually referred to as the **event-related potential (ERP)** in the case of EEG, and **event-related field** in the case of **MEG**. These have characteristic shapes in time (colour Plate 2(c)) and space (Plate 2(d)), which can be analysed into a series of prototypical deflections or **components** in their time course. The signal at any given time point can be interpolated between channels to give a continuous topographic plot over the whole head.

Different recording sites (electrodes) can be more or less sensitive to these components, so it is important to look at signals at many electrode sites in order to identify components accurately. The components are conventionally labelled according to their **polarity** – P(ositive) or N(egative) – and the typical latency of their occurrence. For example, 'auditory N100' refers to a negative potential at frontal electrode sites, usually observed 100 ms after the onset of an auditory stimulus (e.g. a simple tone, a speech sound, etc.).

The strength and pattern of these components can be measured, and their dependence on task requirements, on stimulus parameters, on degree of attention, etc., can be evaluated. Components known to be related to perceptual processing in the tactile, visual, and auditory domains (known as **evoked potentials**, or **evoked magnetic fields**) can be used by clinicians to check the connections between the peripheral and central nervous systems, much like an electrician might use a voltmeter to diagnose a faulty electrical cable.

For example, the presentation of simple tones is normally succeeded by specific components in the EEG signal. These are classified according to their time of occurrence into **brain-stem responses** (until approximately 20 ms after stimulus onset), **middle latency responses** (20–50 ms approx. after onset), and **slow** or **late responses** (later than 50 ms approx. after onset). It is known that the brain-stem responses originate from parts of the brain stem and/or from a cranial nerve (hence their name), while the late responses are cortical in origin. This information is used in objective **ear testing**, which tests the integrity of the auditory system from brain stem to cortex, and is used to screen for possible congenital deafness in newborns and infants, with whom conventional hearing tests that require a behavioural or verbal response to sound cannot be used, and also in persons who are suspected of faking hearing loss for insurance reasons. By detecting abnormalities in these components of the EEG signal, it can be possible to decide at which stage damage to the auditory system has occurred.

2.2.1 Reduction of noise

The measured signal not only contains the signal of interest, but also noise. For example, during the recording, EEG and MEG signals are undergoing slow shifts over time, such that the mean level might differ considerably across channels, though the smaller and faster signal fluctuations are similar. These signal shifts can be due to slow brain activity, but can also be caused by perspiration (in the case of EEG), muscle tension, or other noise sources. Obviously, one should attempt to remove anything from the data that is not related to the processes of interest. The noise level in the averaged data decreases (only) with the square root of the number of trials. This poses a considerable limitation on the duration of an experiment, and should be carefully considered prior to setting up a study. A usual number of trials per experimental condition in EEG and MEG studies on cognition is approximately 50–100, though in some cases this number can be lower. A low number of trials can be compensated for, in part, by recording data from more subjects. In general, however, the rule is 'the more the better'.

Two other standard procedures for reducing noise are generally applied: filtering and baseline correction.

Filtering is applied to a data set to remove any frequencies that are not part of the signal of interest, i.e. the ERP/ERF components under investigation. In most standard experiments on cognitive brain processes, frequencies above 30 Hz are usually not of interest. Furthermore, the high frequency ranges are most prone to contamination by muscle-related noise activity. Therefore, **low-pass filters** are used to attenuate frequencies above a certain **cut-off frequency** (i.e. they 'let pass' the lower frequencies). Analogously, high-pass filters can remove slow signal shifts. A combination of a low-pass and a high-pass filter is called a **band-pass filter**. A typical band-pass filter for ERP/ERF studies would be 0.1–30 Hz, but this depends largely on the signal of interest and the purpose of the study.

In most ERP and ERF studies, a 'baseline interval' is defined as several tens or hundreds of milliseconds before stimulus onset. For each recording channel, the mean signal over this interval is computed, and subtracted from the signal at all time points. This procedure is usually referred to as **baseline correction**. It is crucial in ERP and ERF experiments to ensure that an observed effect (e.g. an amplitude difference between the components evoked by two sorts of stimuli) is not already present in the signal before the stimuli were presented, since such differences could not possibly reflect stimulus effects and must therefore be artefactual (i.e. a result due not to changes in the independent variable but perhaps to noise or to the way equipment is set up).

2.3 Estimating neuronal sources: the inverse problem

The estimation of the sources in the brain that generate the electrical and magnetic activity recorded by EEG or MEG is usually called the **inverse problem**. What makes this a 'problem' is the fact that we are trying to identify the cause of the EEG or MEG signal from its effect, and that unfortunately many different causes might lead to the same effect. This **inverse problem** is comparable to reconstructing a face from its shadow in profile: only some features (e.g. the shape of the nose and chin) are uniquely determined; other features can only be deduced after additional information is received. Or imagine that you see the shadow of an object on the wall of your room, and you want to know what the object is. If you already know that there are only a few objects possible, the choice might be easy. However, in some cases it may be very hard to know what is casting the shadow (e.g. if you just see a square shadow, is it a wardrobe or a bookshelf?). Furthermore, the more similar the shapes of the objects in question, the more difficult it will be to identify which object causes the shadow in question.

Even if the EEG and MEG signals were measured simultaneously at infinitely many points around the head, the information would still be insufficient to uniquely compute the distribution of currents within the brain that generated these signals (this is known as the **Helmholtz principle**, another expression for the inverse problem).

2.3.1 Approaches to deal with the inverse problem

But all is not lost. Researchers can develop models of the underlying activity of the brain and then compare the EEG and MEG data that these models would produce with the data observed in participants. One can distinguish two broad strategies, depending on whether researchers have additional information about the neuronal generators (perhaps from neuropsychological investigations or other neuroimaging data):

1   Approaches that make specific modelling assumptions, like the number of distinct activated brain regions and their approximate location (for example, that there are two focal sources, one in the left, the other in the right auditory cortex, 80 ms after presentation of a tone).

2   Approaches that make as few assumptions as possible, and focus on rough features of the current distribution (for example, that a language task will result in more left-hemispheric activation compared with a mental rotation task).

Examples of these two approaches, and how the models relate to the neuronal sources, are shown in colour Plate 3. In a simulation, two dipoles were placed, one in the left and one in the right hemisphere. The potential distribution produced by both dipoles together is shown as a contour plot in the left image in Plate 3(c) From mere visual inspection of the potential distribution alone, neither the location of the dipoles nor even the number of sources can be deduced. The right image shows a distributed source solution computed from the same data. It exhibits one peak of activation in each hemisphere, around the true dipole locations. Though the 'blurring' inherent to this method does not allow precise localization of the sources, it can provide information about their number (in our example two) and approximate location (here one source in each hemisphere at roughly symmetrical positions). The images on the left and right represent solutions to the same problem (i.e. the source models produce the same potential distribution over 148 recording channels).

If the number of activated brain regions that generate the recorded signal is assumed to be known, but their locations are still to be determined, so-called **dipole models** can be applied (Plate 3(c), left): the locations and orientations of dipoles are systematically varied until the best fit between the predicted and the measured potential is achieved. If the modelling assumptions fit reality well, the result can be very accurate (in the millimetre range for MEG and in the centimetre range for EEG). These methods are usually applied if perceptual processes and early-evoked components are studied (e.g. somatosensory, auditory and visual processes up to 150–200 ms after stimulus onset).

If there is no information about the number of sources, methods with less restrictive modelling assumptions – so-called **distributed source models** – can be used. A large number of dipoles (hundreds or thousands) is distributed across the brain volume or the brain surface. Their strengths are then estimated such that their summed activity explains the measured signal and an additional criterion is fulfilled, e.g. that the overall source strengths is kept minimal ('minimum norm criterion'). An example for such an estimate is shown on the right of Plate 3(c). At least a 'blurred' version of the real source distribution can often be obtained. Peaks in this estimated current distribution might correspond to centres of activity in the real current distribution. These methods are preferred if modelling assumptions for dipole models cannot be justified, such as in complex cognitive tasks or with noisy data.

There is no 'one fits all' in EEG and MEG source estimation. It requires insight into the modelling assumptions of the method as well as experience to choose the right method for a given purpose.

2.4 Statistical analysis of EEG/MEG data

The statistical analysis of EEG/MEG data is as yet not fully standardized, and the strategies researchers employ can vary considerably depending on their hypotheses. The most frequent approach is 'analysis of variance' or ANOVA (see Chapter 4 on quantitative methods). The signal amplitudes for different electrodes, sensors or dipoles are considered as dependent variables, and recorded for each subject (e.g. just as we might measure mean reaction times or error rates per subject in behavioural experiments).

Imagine a so-called **oddball** experiment (the 'oddball paradigm' is discussed in Section 2.5), in which subjects are presented with two different tones: one tone of 600 Hz, which occurs 90 per cent of the time, and another tone of 1,000 Hz, which occurs only 10 per cent of the time. Subjects are required to press different buttons in response to the frequent and rare tones. Does the maximum amplitude of the ERP in a certain time range change as a function of the probability of the tone? In this case, one would first have to decide which time range to analyse. In this kind of oddball experiment, it is known that rare tones produce a so-called **P300 component**, i.e. a positive deflection of the ERP around centro-parietal electrode sites, which usually reaches its maximum around 300 ms after stimulus onset. It would therefore be reasonable to look for the largest peak around 300 ms at the electrode Pz, and to extract the amplitudes at this electrode and this point in time for all subjects. These values would enter the ANOVA as a dependent variable. 'Probability' would be a single, two-level factor allowing for a comparison between values obtained for the presentation of the rare tones and those obtained for the frequent tones. In general, the result is that the amplitude of the P300 is larger for rare tones.

Does only the amplitude change with the tone's probability of occurrence, or could there also be a change of 'Laterality'? In other words, could the rare tones produce larger amplitudes in either the left or right hemisphere compared with the frequent ones? In this case, one would have to extract amplitude values for at least two electrodes, one in the left and one in the right hemisphere (e.g. P5 and P6, left and right of Pz). The ANOVA now has two factors: Probability (rare and frequent) and Laterality (left and right). If the laterality changes with tone probability, one should obtain an interaction between Probability and Laterality. In the case of simple tones, such an interaction is generally not found, although it might be expected for more complex (e.g. language-related) stimuli.

2.5 The auditory oddball paradigm

The oddball paradigm, in which subjects are exposed to a stream of 'standard' stimuli occasionally interrupted by 'deviant' stimuli, is one of the most widely used paradigms in cognitive electrophysiology. This paradigm is easy to perform even by severely impaired subjects, and the corresponding ERP effects have been studied intensively during the last decades. Two major components are usually observed in ERP and ERF studies using oddball paradigms:

1   The **mismatch negativity** or **MMN**: an early component (between approximately 100 and 200 ms) that is independent of the level of attention, and is generally interpreted as a 'preattentive change detection mechanism'.

2   The P300: a component peaking around 300 ms, generally larger when target stimuli (e.g. deviants) have to be detected in a stream of standards. This component is often interpreted in terms of the 'updating of working memory'.

The data presented in Figure 2.3 are taken from Opitz *et al.* (1999). The same 16 subjects participated in EEG as well as in a functional magnetic resonance imaging (fMRI) experiment. ERPs were recorded from 120 electrode sites. The stimulus set consisted of two 200 ms tones (600 Hz and 1,000 Hz). The experiment was divided into 12 'standard' blocks, in which only the low tone was presented 24 times, and 12 'deviant' blocks, in which 16 low and 8 high tones were presented. This design was chosen in order to run the same experimental paradigm both with EEG and fMRI. In different runs, subjects were either told not to attend to the stimuli, but to watch a cartoon video instead ('unattend' condition), or to silently count the high tones ('attend' condition).

The detection of a change within a sequence of stimuli elicits an MMN shortly after 100 ms, independently of the level of attention. Dipole modelling, where the position of the dipoles is based on the position of activations observed in the companion fMRI experiment, suggests that the sources of this MMN component are localized in left and right superior temporal gyri (STG). The later P300 is elicited when the deviant stimuli are relevant to the performance of a task, and the generators were estimated in left and right transverse temporal gyri (TTG). It should be noted, however, that the relationship between EEG/MEG sources and fMRI/PET activity is still not clearly understood. It is generally not straightforward to constrain EEG/MEG source localization by fMRI/PET results. The development of corresponding methods and their empirical evaluation is currently one of the most exciting areas in the field of neuroimaging.

Figure 2.3 The auditory oddball paradigm:
(a) ERP difference waveforms ('standards' (low tones) minus 'deviants' (high tones)) averaged across subjects. Note the early negative deflection at frontal electrode sites (e.g. at Fz around 150 ms) in both conditions (MMN), and the large positive deflection in the 'attend' condition only at posterior electrode sites (P300, e.g. at Pz after 300 ms)
(b) Topography of the MMN (left) and P300 components (right). Both the original data (top) and the prediction of the dipole models (bottom) are shown
(c) Two dipoles fitted to the ERP data explained up to 95 per cent of the data for both the MMN and P300. Dipole locations (as indicated by arrows) were consistent with fMRI activation spots

Source: based on Opitz et al., 1999, Figures 1–5

Summary of Section 2

- EEG and MEG record the electrical activity of the brain millisecond by millisecond, such that they are sensitive to changes in the temporal pattern of cognitive processes.
- They do this only indirectly, which means that the location of corresponding activity in the brain can only be estimated.
- EEG and MEG signals are in principle generated by the same sources inside the brain. However, MEG is less sensitive to deeper and radial sources, but is in turn better in localizing superficial and tangential ones (i.e. those near and approximately parallel to the scalp).
- Data are usually analysed by computing 'event-related potentials/fields' (ERPs/ERFs): data segments are averaged across a large number of trials belonging to the same stimulus category, and then different averages are subtracted from each other to extract the signal specific to a certain cognitive process.

3   Techniques based on metabolism and blood supply

The brain requires a nearly constant supply of oxygen and glucose in order to function properly. Both glucose and oxygen are carried to the brain in the blood supply, via an array of arterial vessels. Although the brain accounts for only about 2 per cent of the body's mass, it consumes about 20 per cent of the body's glucose and oxygen, and receives about 20 per cent of its blood supply. Although the relationship is still not completely understood, activity in neurons is closely linked to glucose consumption, oxygen consumption, and blood flow. Blood in the brain goes to where it is needed: as a local group of neurons becomes active, blood flow in that region increases, as does the amount of oxygen in the blood in that region (**blood oxygenation**). Thus, imaging techniques that are sensitive to blood flow and blood oxygenation can be used to study 'the brain at work'. **Positron emission tomography (PET)**, when used by psychologists, measures how the pattern of blood flow in the brain changes (how it is increased in some areas and decreased in others) as a function of cognitive state. **Functional magnetic resonance imaging (fMRI)** is used by psychologists in a very similar way, to index regional changes in blood oxygenation as a function of cognitive state. We first discuss some of the most common designs used in these neuroimaging experiments, before explaining how the **dependent measure** in these designs (signal, derived from blood flow or blood oxygenation) is obtained in PET and fMRI.

3.1   Experimental design

Neuroimaging experiments are designed to assess relative changes in brain activity (indexed by **regional cerebral blood flow (rCBF)** in the case of PET, or regional changes in blood oxygenation in fMRI) consequent upon changes in stimulus characteristics or task demands. The two most commonly used approaches are subtractive designs and correlational (or parametric) designs.

3.1.1 Subtractive designs

In 1868, the Dutch physiologist Franciscus C. Donders proposed a general method to measure thought processes based on the assumption that tasks can be broken down into component processes (Donders, 1969). One comparison Donders made was between the reaction time to one stimulus presented by itself (simple reaction time) and the reaction time needed to identify a stimulus before responding. Donders believed that the subtraction of the simple reaction time from the identification reaction time would yield the time required for stimulus identification itself. Figure 2.4 gives a similar example in which the time taken to press a key in response (R) to a light coming on (the stimulus S) (Task 1) can be subtracted from the time needed to press the key only when a light of a particular colour is illuminated (Task 2). On the assumption that the identification component in Task 2 can be 'slotted in' between the two components in Task 1, with these other components remaining the same, then the subtraction reveals how long the process of identification takes.

Figure 2.4 Cognitive subtraction. Task 1 involves responding to the detection of a light; Task 2 involves responding to the detection of a light of a particular colour

The same subtractive logic is often used in the design of neuroimaging experiments. That is, if two conditions, *A* and *B*, are identical except that *A* requires a particular cognitive function *f* while *B* does not, then one can identify those cortical regions that are involved in *f* by subtracting the pattern of rCBF observed during *B* from that during *A*. This approach is essentially an extension of Donders's method (Raichle, 1998).

In general, the conditions that are being compared will differ in one of two ways: the stimuli presented during the two conditions may be identical, but the participants may be required to perform different tasks; or the participants may be presented with different kinds of stimuli in each condition, but the task that they are required to perform may be identical. Box 2.1 gives examples of these two approaches.

2.1 — Methods

Subtractive designs

Klein and colleagues (1995) were interested in whether different brain areas are recruited when volunteers use a language they are proficient in but acquired relatively late in life (in this case, French) compared with their native language (English). Participants heard words in English and French, and were asked either to simply repeat what they had heard, or generate synonyms of the words they had heard (in both languages). This latter task, in addition to recruiting areas involved with speech perception and production (as in the repetition tasks) would also recruit areas involved in semantic association and word retrieval and selection (as volunteers 'look for' and select a suitable synonym).

Comparing synonym generation to word repetition, within each language, is an example of the 'same stimuli, different task' approach. In both tasks, subjects heard single words, which they simply repeated in one condition, and to which they generated synonyms in the other. In both English and French, this comparison revealed activation in prefrontal cortex, indicating the importance of this region in the processing of word meaning and in response selection.

Comparing word repetition in the two languages is an example of the 'different stimuli, same task' approach. A small area in the left basal ganglia was observed to be significantly more active when volunteers repeated French compared with English words. This is interesting, since the basal ganglia are known to be involved in skilled motor action, including articulation of words. Perhaps even when English speakers are proficient in French, their motor apparatus has to work 'harder' to pronounce French words.

An elaboration of the idea of cognitive subtraction is the **hierarchical subtractive design**. In studies of this type, conditions are successively 'built up' from cognitive or perceptual components which are assumed to be additive. For example, in a study of speech perception (see Figure 2.5), rest (lying quietly) could be compared with listening to noise bursts, which would activate the auditory system but not the language system. Listening to words and listening to noise bursts would both activate the auditory system, but words would also activate parts of the brain involved in perceiving and understanding language. Repeating words would activate all these regions, and, in addition, regions involved in speech output. Generating synonyms to a heard word, as discussed in Box 2.1, would activate regions involved in semantic search and word retrieval, in addition to areas involved in hearing and repeating words.

Figure 2.5 Example of a PET experiment (a study of verb generation) employing a hierarchical subtractive design. During each 60-second scan, volunteers perform one of the five possible tasks (conditions). Each condition is performed twice in a pseudorandom order, so that each occurs once in the first half of the experiment and once in the last half. Volunteers begin performance of the task just before each injection of radioactively labelled water; then the PET detectors collect data for 60 seconds; then the volunteers stop task performance. A computer reconstructs the data into a whole-brain image showing where radioactively labelled water accumulated during task performance. Scans are separated by a 7–10 minute period in which volunteers lie quietly in the scanner; this is done to permit the radiation level to decline back to a baseline level (see Section 3.2 for more information about the PET method)

Another elaboration of the subtractive approach is the **factorial design**, such as that used in behavioural research. We have already encountered a simple factorial design in the English/French PET study of Klein *et al.* (1995) (see Box 2.1). If we take the two conditions of repetition, and the two conditions of synonym generation, we have described two levels of two factors: Task (Repetition or Generation) and Language (English or French). As in a conventional behavioural experiment with a 2 × 2 factorial design, the data can be analysed to address questions about main effects (What brain areas are active whenever French is used compared with English, across both tasks? What brain areas are more active during synonym generation than repetition, regardless of language?) and interactions (Are there areas in which the activation difference between synonym generation and repetition is greater for French?). Factorial designs are powerful because the experimenter can look at two or more independent variables simultaneously, and also assess whether or not interdependencies exist between these variables.

3.1.2 Correlational/parametric designs

Correlational/parametric designs are used to examine the relationship between a stimulus parameter (such as word presentation rate), or a behavioural response (such as reaction time), and brain activity. Correlational designs are elegant because they avoid many of the complexities of interpretation intrinsic to subtractive designs, including uncertainty about the assumption of additivity of cognitive processes (cf. Friston *et al.*, 1996). Correlation can also be used to assess brain connectivity and how it changes as a function of cognitive state. For example, signal change in one point in the brain can be used to predict activity elsewhere in the brain. If two areas show correlated activity, it is likely that these areas are connected in some way (directly or via another region). As cognitive state changes, so can connections among areas, reflecting recruitment of different functional networks.

We now turn our attention to PET and fMRI techniques themselves – how they work, what their advantages and disadvantages are – before revisiting issues of data processing and analysis in more detail.

3.2   PET: positron emission tomography

3.2.1   How it works

PET cameras are used to measure local concentrations of biologically important compounds (such as glucose, water, neurotransmitters, or drug compounds). Positron-emitting isotopes of oxygen, fluorine, nitrogen, carbon, and other elements are incorporated into glucose, water, or other **neurochemicals** (compounds used by the brain) using chemical reactions, and then these are introduced into the body. (**Positrons** are positively charged electrons that are emitted from the nucleus of unstable (radioactive) isotopes, such as oxygen-15.) The emitted positron combines with an ordinary electron of a nearby atom in an **annihilation reaction**, turning the

Figure 2.6   Coincidence detection in a PET scanner. When high-energy photons (gamma rays) are detected at opposite detectors (A), positron annihilation must have occurred somewhere along the coincidence line (the straight line connecting the two detectors). The intersection of many successively detected coincidence lines, observed over the course of a scan, pinpoints areas of relative concentration of the radioactive label. A computer uses the data gathered by the detectors to construct two- or three-dimensional images that show where the labelled compound (e.g. water (blood), glucose, or other neurochemical) accumulated in the brain

mass of the two particles into **gamma rays** (high-energy light particles) that are emitted at 180 degrees from each other. These photons easily escape from the human body, and can be recorded by a ring of radiation detectors: the PET scanner (see Figure 2.6). By recording the detection of these photons, it is possible to monitor the distribution of neurochemicals, without disturbing their physiological behaviour, with a temporal resolution ranging from several seconds to several minutes, and with a spatial resolution of several millimetres.

3.2.2 Two kinds of PET study

PET is often used to study **resting metabolism**, that is to say, brain activity in the absence of any particular cognitive task. After being injected with the tracer compound, patients are scanned while lying quietly in the scanner. Such metabolic scans are useful for diagnosing brain disease: in some diseases, affected brain tissue is often less metabolically active than healthy tissue, appearing as 'dark areas' on the resulting images.

When psychologists use PET, however, they are generally interested in knowing where activity increases in the brain as a function of a particular cognitive task. These are called **activation PET** studies. Most activation PET studies use oxygen-15 labelled water as a tracer, since: (a) this isotope decays quickly, and so disappears rapidly from the body; (b) blood is mostly composed of water; and (c) water crosses the blood-brain barrier easily. Labelled water is injected into the bloodstream of the volunteer or patient, usually in the arm, and diffuses rapidly throughout the blood supply as the volunteer performs a particular task (listening to a series of words, for example). As brain areas become active (such as auditory cortex, in response to spoken words), blood flow to those areas increases, and this is reflected in an increased concentration of the isotope in that region. Many gamma rays emanate from the region of concentrated isotope and are detected by the PET camera. Thus, activation PET, using labelled water, measures regional cerebral blood flow (rCBF). In most activation PET studies, 8–12 scans are taken, each approximately a minute long, with a 7–10 minute interval between scans; this is long enough for the tracer to disappear from the body before the next injection is given. A single task is performed throughout any given scan. Three to six different tasks (such as listening to words, listening to noise, and resting quietly) are usually tested within a single subject, with approximately 10 subjects in a study (as in Figure 2.5; see Section 3.1.1).

3.2.3 Limitations of PET

The most obvious limitation of activation PET is that blood flow is only an indirect measure of neuronal activity, which is what researchers are really interested in. And changes in blood supply happen several seconds *after* the population of neurons under study has become active. This limitation also applies to functional magnetic resonance imaging and will be discussed in more detail in Section 3.4.1.

Most countries, including the UK, have strict rules regarding the administration of ionizing radiation to ensure the safety of the general public. In the UK, the annual dose to members of the public is limited to 5 milliSieverts (mSv). This overall dose of 5 mSv is comparable to a year of exposure to natural background radiation. All of us are exposed to natural radiation (such as cosmic rays and naturally occurring radon gas) throughout our lives. In the UK, this exposure ranges between 2.5 and

7.8 mSv (in areas with quite high natural concentrations of radon, such as parts of Devon and Cornwall) per year. However, in a typical activation PET study, a participant may experience 8–12 scans, and the total exposure across all of these must not exceed 5 mSv per year. More scans than this are not feasible, since the camera's sensitivity to blood flow depends on the size of dose given in any particular scan. If more scans were taken, then dose per scan would be even smaller. If too little isotope is given, then the camera does not detect gamma rays related to local accumulation of labelled blood.

Regulations in most countries also stipulate that PET cannot be used as a research tool with children or, in the UK, with women of childbearing age. Thus activation PET studies can only be used for research with a subset of the population (men over 18 and postmenopausal women), and only a limited number of experimental conditions can be tested, since only 8–12 scans per volunteer can be taken. Given the limited number of scans, it is difficult to repeat tests with individuals. This limits PET as a tool for investigating processes that occur over a period of time, such as patterns of brain activity before and after learning a skill.

PET is also expensive. In order to create the isotopes that are used as tracers, and to incorporate these into biologically important compounds, an array of sophisticated equipment is required. This equipment is expensive to both operate and maintain, but because most of the isotopes that are used in PET decay quickly, they have to be made in a **cyclotron** adjacent to the camera and as soon as needed. Finally, compared with functional magnetic resonance imaging (fMRI, see Section 3.4), which can answer many of the same kinds of research questions, activation PET studies, in practice, usually have quite poor temporal resolution (often greater than 60 seconds) and poor spatial resolution (the spatial resolution of activation PET depends on a number of factors including the tracer that is used, but is generally in the order of 10 mm or more).

3.2.4 Advantages of PET

PET is a quiet imaging technique, and high-fidelity sound delivery can be easily used with it, making it a valuable tool in auditory research. Unlike fMRI, PET is compatible with the metallic and magnetic components contained in many implants, such as pacemakers and cochlear implants. Furthermore, unlike most fMRI systems, PET permits the researcher to be in close contact with the patient or volunteer: the volunteer is scanned for at most two minutes at a time, preceded and followed by contact with the researcher or radiographer. Also, PET scanners only encircle the head, leaving the body mostly open to the room, and are consequently less likely than MR scanners to provoke claustrophobic reactions.

Most importantly, PET is not restricted to oxygen as a tracer: other radioisotopes can be incorporated into other compounds that are active in the brain (neurochemicals) and that bind specifically to brain receptors of various types. For example, brain receptors for the neurotransmitter dopamine (**neurotransmitters** are chemicals that act as messengers between cells in the brain) are known to play a crucial role in many cognitive processes, in motor function, and in emotion. A compound called **raclopride**, incorporating a radioactive isotope of carbon, binds to a subtype of dopamine receptors. Another compound, **fluorodopa** (labelled with a radioactive isotope of fluorine) mimics a chemical precursor of dopamine. These compounds can be used to study the dopamine system both in normal individuals and in those suffering from disorders that affect it (Parkinson's disease, schizophrenia, depression, addiction). Many other compounds, specialized for study of other neurotransmitter systems, currently exist and more are being developed. This sort of research is not very common because it is very hard to do: complex chemical reactions are required to produce radioactive compounds that are specific to particular brain receptors.

Although tracers other than oxygen are usually used in resting metabolic PET studies, some recent experiments have used such tracers in activation studies. These experiments explore the effects of cognitive state on activity within neurotransmitter systems. For example, in one PET study, raclopride was given to 8 men and they were scanned twice, once while playing a video game with a monetary reward, and once while staring at a blank screen (the control task). The results showed that playing the game was more associated with dopamine release and binding with dopamine receptors in a part of the brain (the **ventral striatum**) that is known from animal research to be involved in the appreciation of reward. Furthermore, this increase in dopamine release and binding correlated with level of performance achieved on the video game (Koepp *et al.*, 1998). Thus PET is a unique tool with considerable potential for mapping and studying neurotransmitter systems and neurochemically specific processes in both healthy volunteers and in patient groups.

3.3 SPECT: single photon emission computerized tomography

In SPECT, as in PET, a small amount of a radioactive compound is injected into the body. The compounds that are used generally mimic the action of one of the brain's neurochemicals, and so accumulate in the brain in areas where the metabolic process involving the compound of interest typically occurs. As with PET, gamma rays are emitted from the compound, and these are detected by a **gamma camera**. A computer is used to reconstruct the brain image in three dimensions. Like PET, this imaging technique is used to measure metabolism throughout the brain. Generally, SPECT tracers are more limited than PET tracers in the kinds of brain activity they can monitor. SPECT tracers also deteriorate more slowly than many PET tracers, which means that SPECT scans usually last longer than PET scans do, and much more time must elapse between scans to ensure that radiation levels fall to baseline. However, because SPECT tracers are longer lasting, compounds can be synthesized in centralized laboratories and then shipped to facilities where SPECT is used, so SPECT requires much less specialized technical equipment and staff than PET. While PET is more versatile than SPECT and produces more detailed images with a higher degree of resolution, particularly of deeper brain structures, SPECT is much less expensive.

3.4 fMRI: functional magnetic resonance imaging

The last few years has seen a rapid shift of emphasis in functional imaging away from PET activation studies towards functional MRI. Not only is MRI more widely available than PET, but with no associated radiation load it has quickly become an attractive alternative for cognitive studies in healthy volunteers. PET radiation limits mean that few observations can be obtained per volunteer; many more scans can be acquired using fMRI. This results in much stronger signals, making it possible to study brain activity in individual volunteers (not just in groups), so that studies of individual differences are possible. Not only has this development reduced the need for group 'averaging' within studies, but it also allows studies to be repeated in individual volunteers. One consequence is that many longer-term dynamic cognitive processes, such as learning, can be examined effectively. However, it is probably the superior spatial and temporal resolution of fMRI over PET that most clearly established fMRI as a major tool for the study of human cognition.

MRI is the general name for a broad class of techniques that use magnetic fields and radio waves to image the structure, organization, and function of biological systems without injecting radioactive tracers. Two of these techniques are used commonly in psychology and cognitive neuroscience. Structural MRI reveals the anatomical structure of the brain (see Figure 2.1), whereas functional MRI (fMRI) measures regional levels of blood oxygenation, which are assumed to reflect the volunteer's cognitive state.

3.4.1 How MRI works

If you have ever played with magnets, you will know that magnetic fields are not stopped by materials that are electrically insulating. For example, a magnet under a thin wooden table will move a paperclip on its surface; similarly, magnetic fields pass easily through the skull. A large cylindrical magnet around a volunteer's head and upper body creates a strong magnetic field, with a direction that is parallel to the volunteer's body. Other magnets are applied so that the strength of this field changes systematically across the head. Various atomic nuclei, particularly the proton

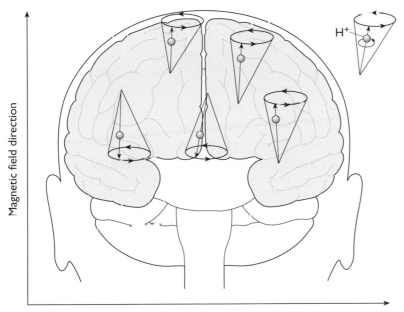

Figure 2.7 Hydrogen nuclei (protons) aligning in a strong magnetic field in the head of a volunteer. Each proton spins about an axis; in turn, the axis also wobbles or precesses around the axis of the magnetic field

nucleus of the hydrogen atom (which is very common in the brain, since there are two atoms of hydrogen in every water molecule and the brain is mostly water), align themselves with the magnetic field. These hydrogen protons, which spin anyway, precess (like the wobble of spinning tops) about the axis of the applied magnetic field at a characteristic frequency that depends on the strength of the field that they are in (see Figure 2.7). Initially, the protons precess (wobble) out of synchrony with each other. When radiofrequency energy is applied, the protons suddenly become synchronized in their movements, but, because they all precess at different rates, they drift out of synchrony again quite soon. However, as this happens they release energy. The frequency of the energy they release depends on the field strength they experience; that is, their position in the head. Sensors just outside the head detect the frequency of these energies, and a computer can be used to reconstruct an image of the distribution of protons and, with it, different tissues (e.g. grey matter, white matter, blood, cerebrospinal fluid) of the brain. This tissue contrast is coded in greyscale in the images.

Functional MRI (fMRI) relies on the different magnetic properties of oxygenated and deoxygenated blood, and allows scientists to observe how the relative concentrations of oxygenated and deoxygenated blood change with cognitive state. Oxygen is carried to the brain in haemoglobin molecules in red blood cells. The bright red blood in the arterial supply relinquishes its oxygen to brain tissue in capillary beds (where oxyhaemoglobin is converted into deoxyhaemoglobin). Purplish deoxygenated blood flows away from capillary beds in the draining venules and veins. As neural activity increases in a part of the brain, more oxygen is extracted from the blood, but blood flow and blood volume in that part also increase. The blood volume increases more than is necessary – it overcompensates for the increase in oxygen consumption. (Imagine every fire engine in London arriving on the doorstep of a chip-pan fire in Notting Hill!) More oxygenated blood is supplied than is needed, which has the effect of decreasing the concentration of deoxyhaemoglobin in the system of venules and veins draining the patch of active tissue (see Figure 2.8(a)). Since deoxyhaemoglobin and oxyhaemoglobin have different magnetic properties, this change in concentration alters the magnetic field strength in the region, which is reflected in the patterns of energy released by protons during scanning. This effect is known as **blood oxygen level dependent (BOLD) contrast**. Thus the fMRI signal is only a secondary consequence of neural activity and does not measure neural activity directly. The **haemodynamic response**, which is the change in BOLD that occurs with a change in neural activity in a particular brain region, happens much more slowly than activity in neurons does. It takes 4–5 seconds to develop after neural activity increases, and takes as long again to decay after neural activity stops (see Figure 2.8(b)). Thus, when the experimental condition changes, BOLD response takes 4–5 seconds to change also. This is called the **haemodynamic lag**. This sluggish response limits our ability to know exactly when a bit of brain tissue actually became active after stimulus presentation, but since the lag is relatively constant, the timing of two or more events relative to each other can be measured with greater precision; potentially within a few hundreds of milliseconds (Menon and Kim, 1999).

(a)

(b)

Figure 2.8 Blood oxygen level dependent (BOLD) contrast and the haemodynamic response function:

(a) Functional MRI scans are exquisitely sensitive to subtle fluctuations in magnetic field strength. Oxyhaemoglobin, found in arterial blood, and deoxyhaemoglobin, found in venous blood, have different magnetic properties and when their relative proportions in the blood change, as happens when a patch of neural tissue becomes active, the resulting change in the local magnetic field can be detected

(b) The metabolic change described in (a) is not instantaneous: it takes several seconds to develop (haemodynamic lag), and equally long to settle back to baseline. The example here sketches, for a point in auditory cortex, what the percentage change in BOLD (from a resting level) might be as a function of time since hearing someone snap their fingers (at time 0). This is called the haemodynamic response function (HRF)

Source: (a) adapted from P Jezzard, http://www.fmrib.ox.ac.uk/fmri_intro/brief.html

The spatial resolution of fMRI is mostly limited by the strength of the magnet used to generate the main magnetic field: the stronger the magnet, the finer the potential resolution. This is for two closely related reasons. First, stronger magnets are just more sensitive, so small signal changes (small areas of activated tissue) can be detected more easily, and two such small regions of activation can be more easily distinguished. Second, more sensitivity means that instead of picking up signal in veins (which produce large signal changes), signal in small venules and in the capillary bed can be detected. Since venules and capillaries are much closer to the active neural tissue than veins are – veins can be several millimetres away from actually active tissue – spatial resolution is improved. The fact that signal in veins can be mistaken for signal in brain tissue, unless precautions are taken, is one limitation of fMRI. Further limitations and advantages are detailed in the next sections.

3.4.2 Limitations

As with PET, fMRI is sensitive to changes in the local blood supply when a population of neurons becomes active. It is only an indirect measure of neural activity, and since changes in blood supply happen slowly, temporal resolution is limited, and is not as good as with EEG and MEG.

We have already explained how, since large BOLD changes can occur in veins, apparent activation can be located at some distance 'downstream' from brain tissue that is actually active. Without knowing where veins are located in each subject (like brain anatomy, the organization of blood vessels, particularly on the venous side, can be very different from person to person), venous activation can be mistaken for tissue activation. This obviously makes it difficult to infer confidently that the tissue in a region of significant signal change is actually involved in the cognitive process being studied (the real activated tissue may be up to a centimetre or more 'upstream'). There are several ways of getting around this problem. First, more powerful magnets, or different imaging protocols, can be used to improve signal strength in venules and capillaries. Second, MRI can also be used to make maps of blood vessel distribution (**angiograms**) in each individual: these maps can be compared to patterns of activation to identify and eliminate activation in vessels.

Several other limitations of the fMRI technique are based on the physics of the BOLD signal. BOLD is a special case of a subtle fluctuation in local magnetic field strength, which can be detected with specialized imaging protocols. Such imaging protocols are necessarily sensitive to all subtle changes in local field strength, including those caused by the brain's structure itself, not just by the state of the local blood supply. For example, air-filled pockets in the head (like the sinuses) have a very different effect on local magnetic field strength than do brain tissues: thus the magnetic field changes quite dramatically at the front of the head where the sinuses are. Because fMRI actually requires a quite uniform magnetic field, these relatively dramatic changes in field strength produce decreased signal (sometimes no signal at all) in affected regions. For this reason, inferior frontal and temporal cortex, close to such air pockets, can be hard to image. Unfortunately these regions are interesting to psychologists since they are implicated in decision-making behaviour and smell (orbitofrontal cortex), emotion (amygdala), memory (hippocampus) and language (lateral temporal cortex). An inability to 'see' these areas properly using fMRI makes it difficult (but not impossible – again, strategies to minimize this problem are in quite common use) to use as a research tool in these areas.

Fluctuations in field strength (**field inhomogeneities**) can also produce geometric distortion in images, apparently 'stretching' some parts and 'squashing' others, resulting in an image that is quite a different shape from the real brain.

A popular way to 'correct' images for this problem is to map the magnetic field inhomogeneities for each volunteer.

Other limitations of MR are purely practical. First, the strong magnetic field means that volunteers with ferromagnetic implants (such as pacemakers, or pins to repair broken bones, or most types of cochlear implant) cannot be scanned safely. It also makes for a difficult experimental situation, since totally magnet-compatible stimulus-delivery systems (video projectors, headphones, response boxes) must be used. However, most fMRI systems are now equipped with a video projector which can present a picture (usually the screen of the computer controlling the stimulus delivery), headphones through which sounds can be presented, and response devices such as a buttonbox or joystick.

When the scanner is acquiring data it is very noisy – noise levels up to 130 dB are common. This is loud enough to damage unprotected ears. This noise is unpleasant, and even when partially blocked with earplugs can be distracting. Given this high level of background noise, special care must be taken when designing studies using sound. The most common approach is to scan intermittently, not continuously, alternating several seconds of sound presentation with 1 or 2 seconds of scanning. In this way, sounds are presented in a quiet background, and the delay in the haemodynamic response (see Figure 2.8(b)) means that a scan taken 4–6 seconds after stimulus presentation will optimally detect elevated signal due to that stimulus.

The data quality of fMRI is seriously compromised by subject movement, so subjects must stay perfectly still during scanning. This also means that they cannot speak, so a task requiring speech or other movements of the head is not practical. Most fMRI tasks involve either keypress or joystick responses. The restriction on movement means that patient groups with movement disorders can be difficult to scan. Finally, some subjects cannot tolerate the confined space of the MRI scanner.

3.4.3 Advantages

fMRI can be repeated within subjects, so it can be used to study processes that change over time, for example as a function of development, or as an individual recovers from injury or stroke, or acquires a new skill. It has quite good temporal and spatial resolution, and these both continue to improve as techniques are refined.

An fMRI scan can produce an image of BOLD signal, covering most or all of the brain, as fast as every second. If an experiment is targeted at a particular brain area (the auditory cortex, for example), then a small brain volume consisting mostly of the area of interest can be scanned, and **acquisition time** (the time required to take one scan) can be reduced even further. In principle, fMRI can produce an image that distinguishes structures less than a millimetre apart, and this potential is being realized. (For example, in visual cortex, cells that respond preferentially to lines of a given orientation are arranged into columns, which in the cat are half a millimetre wide and approximately 1 mm apart. Kim and colleagues (2000) were able to use fMRI to map such orientation columns in the visual cortex of the cat.)

In summary, fMRI is an increasingly common tool that psychologists use to determine how different parts of the brain are specialized for different cognitive processes. Although there are several limitations to the technique, it is a field that is growing and developing rapidly. We shall now discuss how imaging data must be processed before they can be analysed. In general, these stages of processing apply to both PET and fMRI. Exceptions will be clearly noted.

3.5   Image processing and analysis

The analysis of imaging data is a multistage process (see colour Plate 4). First, the scans must be **reconstructed**. The raw data that is collected in PET, SPECT and fMRI does not resemble an image. A mathematical transform, such as Fourier analysis, is required to turn the data into a set of images: **the image time series** (the sequence of images acquired over time). Additional steps are then often required for fMRI data to correct for artefact and distortion. We now review the most important processing steps required for reconstructed images to be prepared for the stage of processing that is closest to the researcher's heart – the statistical analysis that reveals where significant activation related to experimental variables occurred.

First, although movement of the head is generally restrained in some way (by lying in a moulded helmet, or with a headpiece), some movement is nevertheless inevitable over the course of a scanning session (several minutes to a few hours). Any movement means that the position of the brain within the images will vary over time. Thus, the images need to be **realigned**, bringing them all back into registration, correcting for head movement.

One concept that is almost universally used in functional imaging is that of a **standard space** – a standard space provides a way to locate positions in the head (in three dimensions) and allows comparison among different brains (see colour Plate 5). First, an imaginary line is drawn between the **anterior commissure (AC)** and the **posterior commissure (PC)** – two small brain structures that are in very similar positions from person to person. This is the y-axis, and defines front–back (see Plate 5(a) and (b)). Another axis (x) is perpendicular to y, also goes through the AC, and defines left–right (Plate 5(b)). A final axis, z, is perpendicular to the first two, also intersects the AC, and defines up–down (Plate 5(a) and (b)). All three axes intersect, or pass through the origin, at the AC. These axes define the **standardized stereotaxic coordinate system**, sometimes called the **Talairach coordinate system** after an influential brain atlas (Talairach and Tournoux, 1988). Any location in the brain can be indexed by values of these three coordinates, using units that are approximately a millimetre (Plate 5(c)).

Spatial normalization (see colour Plate 4) refers to the process by which brain volumes are changed in shape, size, and orientation so they approximately match that of a **template**, in standard space. A template is usually an average of many representative individual brain volumes. This is done so brains of different subjects (who will have brains of different shapes and sizes) can be easily compared, and so data can be averaged across subjects. It also allows a researcher to match up low-resolution functional data with a high-resolution anatomical image, so activations can be precisely located with respect to brain cortical anatomy. **Anatomical landmarks**, such as the **anterior commissure**, the **Sylvian fissure**, and the **interhemispheric fissure**, will be in an (almost) identical position in all normalized brains. (Brains are all very different, however, and even after spatial normalization some anatomical variability remains.)

When brains are spatially normalized, a particular set of stereotaxic coordinates refers to the same brain region in everyone (see Plate 5(c)). This permits the rescarcher to use **reference atlases** which are in the same space as the template, and which give, for each set of x, y, z coordinates, detailed information about the brain at that point: for instance, atlases can provide information about the likely tissue type, anatomical structure, and what other brain regions might be connected.

It should be noted that sometimes researchers are interested in knowing more about what is different in the anatomy and pattern of activation across individuals, and are not so interested in what is common. In such cases, spatial normalization will be removing some of the differences that interest the researcher.

After normalization, data are usually **spatially smoothed**, meaning that the activation at each point is replaced by a weighted average of the activation measured not just at that point, but at all neighbouring points. This has three benefits. First, it improves power, making activations easier to detect. Second, it ensures that the data conform to the assumptions of the statistical model that will be used to determine the significance of the activations. Third, it compensates for the fact that the same activation might be in slightly different places across individuals, since structural and functional anatomy will not be identical even after spatial normalization.

The disadvantage of spatial smoothing is that it reduces spatial resolution, since the signal is 'smeared out' over adjacent regions. This effect is generally greater in PET data than in fMRI data: in PET data, two activations up to 2 cm apart can be smeared together to appear as one, whereas in fMRI, once activations are more than one centimetre apart, they usually appear as separate. The experimenter can change the amount of smoothing in order to examine whether what is apparently a single blob after smoothing might actually arise from two or more discrete but neighbouring locations.

The final step before data analysis is **temporal filtering**. As with EEG and MEG data (see Section 2.2.1), noise in fMRI data can be removed by filtering. For example, it is common to use a high-pass filter in order to remove slowly varying components in the time series which may be due to physiological effects or to scanner-related drifts in baseline signal. Once this is done, the data are (finally!) ready for statistical analysis.

3.6   Data analysis

3.6.1   Predicting how signal will change over time, and testing such models

The most common way to analyse imaging data is to set up a model that predicts how the signal in the brain will change over scans if it is related to stimulus presentation or task performance. For the PET example in Figure 2.5, regions of the brain that are uniquely involved in synonym generation would be expected to show greater signal in scans 2 and 10 (when subjects were performing the synonym generation task) than in scans 3 and 6 (when they were repeating words, a condition that is closely matched in its other cognitive demands to synonym generation). Each point in the brain is tested separately; that is, at each point in the brain, paired t-tests (over subjects) would indicate whether the signal is higher during synonym generation than during word repetition.

In fMRI, since scans are taken much more often, the haemodynamic response function (HRF) (see Section 3.4.1) must be taken into account when predicting how measured activation will change over time, as a function of stimulus or task. The **data analysis** stage in colour Plate 4 shows a block design in which sound alternates between being 'on' for several seconds and 'off' for an equal period of time. Because of the HRF, the BOLD signal that would be predicted from this design would not increase until a few seconds into the 'on' periods, and then would stay elevated for a few seconds after the sound has been turned off. At each point in the brain, regression equations (see Chapter 4 on quantitative methods) are used to test how well the model fits the observed signal change over scans. The goodness of fit is indexed by **parameter estimates**. The larger the parameter estimate at a given point in the brain, the better the model fits at that point.

3.6.2 Correction for multiple comparisons

Statistical tests are carried out at each of several thousand points in the brain, independently (200,000 points would not be unusual). If we set the significance threshold to 0.05, which is conventional for single statistical tests, then it will be practically guaranteed that one of the tests will reach significance by chance alone (i.e. it will generate a false positive or Type I error – see Chapter 4 on quantitative methods). Indeed, with so many tests, there are likely to be many Type I errors. How can we distinguish between these false positives, and those comparisons where the signal was truly elevated for experimental reasons? We must correct for the fact that so many tests are being carried out: we need a **multiple-comparisons correction**. This can be done in several ways, but such **statistical thresholding** always has the effect of increasing the statistical threshold at which something is judged to be significant. The **activation image** (see Plate 4) shows which points in the brain are activated at a particular (specified) level of significance, usually $p < 0.05$ corrected for multiple comparisons.

Sometimes, researchers have predictions about where in the brain they are expecting to find activation. In such cases, they do not need to correct for tests conducted over the whole brain, just for the tests conducted in the region in which they are interested. The statistical criterion for significance is therefore lower than if a correction had been applied based on tests over the whole brain. The smaller the region they are interested in, based on their hypotheses and on previous work, the smaller the correction needs to be. It is usually helpful in imaging studies to have **anatomical hypotheses**, based on existing literature, about where activation is likely to be observed when perceiving a particular kind of stimulus or performing a particular task.

Summary of Section 3

- PET and fMRI are sensitive to changes in regional blood flow and blood oxygenation: these are indirect measures of neural activity.
- PET requires the administration of a small dose of radiation. Only a limited number of scans can be taken, and it cannot be used as a research tool with children or with women of childbearing age.

- PET can also be used to examine activity within specific neurochemical pathways in the brain, so that neurochemically specific changes as a function of cognitive state can be assessed.

- SPECT is very similar to PET in the way that it works. It has generally poorer spatial and temporal resolution, but is much cheaper to use.

- Imaging data must be extensively processed before they can be analysed. Data processing steps include realignment, spatial normalization, spatial smoothing, and temporal filtering.

- Data analysis is usually conducted independently at every point in the brain. Models that predict signal change over scans are tested against observed values. If all points in the brain are tested, significance thresholds must be adjusted to control for Type I errors (or false positives). Alternatively, researchers can restrict their analyses to the part of the brain they are interested in, thereby reducing the multiple-comparisons problem and permitting use of lower statistical thresholds.

4   Transcranial magnetic stimulation (TMS)

In TMS, a brief current is induced in brain tissue through the scalp and skull, using a brief magnetic pulse delivered via a coil (about the size of a hairdryer) placed over the head (see colour Plate 6). The magnetic field, which is quite strong although very brief, passes through the scalp and skull and into the brain. The shape of the coil determines the properties and size of the field: a **figure-8 coil**, which produces a very strong and focused field at the brain location that is deep relative to the crossing in the '8', is the most popular. The induced current in the brain then renders the local tissue more or less active, depending on the TMS technique that is employed. TMS is non-invasive, is apparently free of serious side effects (if used properly; see BioMag Laboratory, 2001), and has considerable potential as a research, diagnostic, and even therapeutic tool.

As a research tool for exploring the mapping of cognitive functions in the brain (to which we will restrict our discussion), TMS is used to temporarily and reversibly disrupt normal brain function in healthy subjects. This approach is conceptually similar to classic neuropsychology, in which patients with focal brain damage are carefully assessed for evidence of cognitive deficits. Any impaired cognitive function is assumed to rely on the damaged bit of brain. In TMS, activity in an area thought to be necessary for the performance of a particular function can be temporarily interrupted, and then performance on tasks relevant to that function can be assessed. Normal function resumes quickly after actual stimulation has stopped, and so tests are usually administered at the same time as the TMS pulses.

Because the field is created on the surface of the head, there is a trade-off between the size of the brain area that is stimulated and the depth to which the stimulation can reach. Even the strongest and most focused fields cannot penetrate very much further than the surface of the cortex, so that only surface locations (including motor cortex and other frontal areas) are suitable for study. Also, the temporalis muscle, which lies between the scalp and the skull over the temporal lobe, can be caused to contract quite painfully with TMS stimulation, and so TMS is not often used over the temporal lobe.

TMS, like neuropsychology, provides information about what parts of the brain are critical for particular cognitive functions. This is unlike fMRI and PET, which cannot differentiate between areas showing activity that is merely correlated with a particular cognitive function, and areas that are essential to the function.

Summary of Section 4

- TMS can be used to disrupt brain function temporarily. When used properly, it is a safe way to induce a 'reversible lesion' in a particular region of the brain, to determine whether that region is critically involved in the performance of a given task.
- It is only suitable for use with regions on the surface of the brain, and cannot easily be used to study function in the temporal lobe.

5 Choosing a technique

In general, choosing which neuroimaging technique to use for a particular purpose requires researchers to consider a number of different factors. Try the following activity.

ACTIVITY 2.1

There is a theory that states that speech perception is not purely auditory. The hypothesis is that when people hear speech, it automatically activates motor regions involved in pronouncing speech sounds. Colour Plate 7 shows where motor areas related to speech production are likely to be. Try to think of ways in which you could use two different techniques you have learned about to evaluate this theory. Note down the reasons for your choice of technique (why you chose the ones you did, and why you didn't choose the others). How might you set up an experiment to evaluate the theory? What kind of volunteers would you recruit? What kind of experimental design would you use? What would you measure? How would you establish whether you had a significant effect? Note down your answers to these questions. Would the results reveal what areas might be involved in speech perception versus those absolutely necessary for speech perception?

COMMENT

The most appropriate techniques, given the question, are TMS and fMRI. MEG/EEG aren't useful since the question is about *where* in the brain activation is observed, and fine temporal resolution isn't really necessary. PET and SPECT both have a radiation load, and, since this experiment can be performed in normal volunteers (without metallic implants), fMRI is most suitable. An argument could be made that PET is better since this would necessarily be an auditory study and fMRI is noisy, but fMRI can be used for auditory studies as long as they are designed properly. Specifically, the fMRI study should use intermittent (sparse) imaging, where stimulus presentation is alternated with scan acquisition. Experimental design could either be parametric (possibly varying rate or amount of speech) or subtractive. If subtractive, then the experimental conditions should involve listening to speech (either isolated sounds, single words, or sentences). Control conditions should include one that uses non-speech sounds matched to the speech sounds on duration (as in the hierarchical subtraction PET example, Figure 2.5). The analysis would either look for regions that correlated with the parametric factor (in the case of a parametric design) or regions in which activation during experimental conditions was higher than during control conditions. Since a region of interest is included in the hypothesis, the problem of multiple comparisons can be lessened, and the significance threshold used can be more liberal than if tests were conducted over the whole brain.

A TMS experiment would involve delivering TMS over the inferior motor region while the volunteer hears speech, and then testing perception or comprehension for the stimulus. This could be compared with TMS over other regions of the brain (not expected to be involved in speech perception) while the volunteer hears speech. Any stimulus recall, recognition or comprehension test, administered after the speech stimulus (and TMS pulse), could be the dependent measure. Changes in performance on the task would be examined as a function of brain area stimulated: if the inferior motor region is necessary for speech perception, performance will be impaired after TMS stimulation there. If the motor region is either involved but not critical or is not involved at all, task performance will not change as a function of stimulation site.

6   Summary and conclusions

This chapter has introduced you to several methods for the study of normal brain function in healthy volunteers. These are summarized in Table 2.1. Most of these techniques are also popular for use with patients, to examine brain function in people with specific diseases or mental disorders. EEG and MEG give excellent temporal resolution and are sensitive to neuronal activity directly, although they reflect aggregate activity over large groups of neurons. It is hard, without knowing exactly how many groups of neurons are active, to locate EEG and MEG activity with any precision. PET, SPECT and fMRI are sensitive to local changes in brain metabolism, particularly blood flow and the oxygenation state of blood. These are indirectly related to neuronal activity and happen much more slowly, so temporal resolution is not very good. However, these metabolic changes happen in or very close to active neural tissue, and so sources of activation can be located with confidence. PET and SPECT can also be used to study the relationship between specific neurotransmitter systems and cognitive function. Finally, TMS can be used to temporarily inactivate neural tissue close to the skull, in order to determine the importance of that region of the brain for particular cognitive functions.

Table 2.1 A summary of methods used to study the relationship between brain and behaviour in normal volunteers

Technique	Spatial resolution	Temporal resolution	Physiological basis
EEG	>10 mm*	1 ms or less	Summed electrical activity over large groups of neurons
MEG	>5 mm*	1 ms or less	Summed magnetic fields produced by large groups of active neurons
PET	5–20 mm[†]	10 sec.–minutes[†]	Radioactive decay occurring where labelled compound (water in blood, neurochemical) has accumulated
SPECT	20 mm	minutes	Radioactive decay occurring where labelled compound (neurochemical) has accumulated
fMRI	< 5 mm	200 ms–1 sec.[‡]	Magnetic field fluctuations produced by local changes in the proportions of oxyhaemoglobin and deoxyhaemoglobin in blood
TMS	5–10 mm	< ½ sec.	Strong focal magnetic field transiently disrupts activity in large group of neurons

* A general reliable figure cannot be given, since for both EEG and MEG spatial resolution depends on several factors such as modelling assumptions, number of sensors, or signal-to-noise ratio.

[†] Spatial and temporal resolution in PET depends on the compound that is used: compounds that act specifically within particular neurotransmitter systems can take longer to accumulate detectable signal but can be localized with greater precision (since we know where these neurotransmitter systems are found) than labelled water.

[‡] The lower bound of this range refers specifically to when the timings of two events are measured relative to each other within the same brain area of the same subject.

Each of these techniques has its unique advantages and disadvantages. As technology progresses, we can expect the temporal and spatial resolution of all of these tools to improve somewhat, although we are near the practical limits of what is possible already. A major challenge for the coming years will be to combine data from these different methods in order to overcome the limitations of any individual technique. For example, combining EEG and fMRI would give us the excellent temporal resolution of EEG combined with the excellent spatial resolution of fMRI. Combining data across these tools will provide pictures of the functional organization of the brain that are unprecedented in their detail and richness.

Now that you have read this chapter you can reinforce and extend your learning by reading an original journal article associated with it. The journal articles are available through the DD303 website. Remember these are original journal articles, so the style is different from that in this *Methods Companion* and don't be too concerned if you can't follow every detail.

Further reading

Cabeza, R. and Kingstone, A. (2001) *Handbook of Functional Neuroimaging of Cognition*, Cambridge, MA, MIT Press/Triliteral.

Kertesz, A. (1994) *Localization and Neuroimaging in Neuropsychology*, New York, Academic Press.

Toga, A.W. and Mazziotta, J.C. (2000) *Brain Mapping: The Methods*, New York, Academic Press.

References

BioMag Laboratory, Helsinki University Central Hospital (2001) *Safety of TMS*, www.biomag.hus.fi/tms/safety.html (accessed 25 October 2010).

Churchland, P.S. and Sejnowski, T.J. (1988) 'Perspectives on cognitive neuroscience', *Science*, vol.242, pp.741–5.

Cohen, M.S. and Bookheimer, S.Y. (1994) 'Localization of brain function using magnetic resonance imaging', *Trends in Neurosciences*, vol.17, pp.268–77.

Donders, F. (1969) 'On the speed of mental processes', in Koster, W.G. (ed.) *Acta Psychologica, Attention and Performance II*, Amsterdam, North-Holland Publishing.

Friston, K.J., Price, C.J., Fletcher, P., Moore, C., Frackowiak, R.S. and Dolan, R.J. (1996) 'The trouble with cognitive subtraction', *Neuroimage*, vol.4, pp.97–104.

George, M.S. (2003) 'Stimulating the brain', *Scientific American*, vol.289, no.3, pp.67–73.

Kim, D.S., Duong, T.Q. and Kim, S.G. (2000) 'High-resolution mapping of iso-orientation columns by fMRI', *Nature Neuroscience*, vol.3, pp.164–9.

Klein, D., Milner, B., Zatorre, R.J., Meyer, E. and Evans, A.C. (1995) 'The neural substrates underlying word generation: a bilingual functional-imaging study', *Proceedings of the National Academy of Sciences of the USA*, vol.92, pp.2899–903.

Koepp, M.J., Gunn, R.N., Lawrence, A.D., Cunningham, V.J., Dagher, A., Jones, T., Brooks, D.J., Bench, C.J. and Grasby, P.M. (1998) 'Evidence for striatal dopamine release during a video game', *Nature*, vol.393, pp.266–8.

Menon, R.S. and Kim, S.G. (1999) 'Spatial and temporal limits in cognitive neuroimaging with fMR', *Trends in Cognitive Sciences*, vol.3, pp.207–16.

Opitz, B., Mecklinger, A., Von Cramon, D.Y. and Kruggel, F. (1999) 'Combining electrophysiological and hemodynamic measures of the auditory oddball', *Psychophysiology*, vol.36, pp.142–7.

Raichle, M.E. (1998) 'Behind the scenes of functional brain imaging: a historical and physiological perspective', *Proceedings of the National Academy of Sciences of the USA*, vol.95, pp.765–72.

Talairach, J. and Tournoux, P. (1988) *Co-planar Stereotaxic Atlas of the Human Brain. 3-Dimensional Proportional System: An Approach to Cerebral Imaging*, New York, Thieme.

Cognitive neuropsychology

Chapter 3

Ashok Jansari

1 Introduction: why study damaged brains?

If one of the main goals of cognitive psychology is to understand normal human behaviour, then why do cognitive neuropsychologists study damaged brains? Craik puts it succinctly:

> In any well-made machine one is ignorant of the working of most of the parts – the better they work the less we are conscious of them ... it is only a fault which draws attention to the existence of a mechanism at all.
>
> *Craik, 1943*

The human cognitive system is so finely tuned, having evolved over millions of years, that whereas we may be conscious of some aspects of how and why we do things (e.g. how we plan the steps to do a load of laundry so that colours don't run between clothes), details of our most striking abilities (e.g. how you manage to translate the patterns of black ink on this page into an understanding of what I am trying to say) are not available to conscious report. Cognitive psychology is predicated on the assumption that details of such cognitive mechanisms can be inferred through the careful and imaginative use of experimentation with normal human participants. Cognitive neuropsychology is predicated on the somewhat different belief that only when the intact system malfunctions is it possible to get a real sense of the complexity of the mechanisms involved.

As an analogy, imagine the workings of my broken-down car. Cars are highly complex systems whose detailed design is known to engineers and mechanics but not to me: my car might break down for a number of reasons that only a mechanic or engineer could clarify. I could ask them what caused the breakdown – get them to explain how the broken part(s), such as the fan belt, works. Such an explanation would reveal that the car is made up of functionally distinct components and the contribution that the faulty part normally makes to the car's functioning. If I was particularly unfortunate, my car might break down again. This time suppose the mechanic points out that the gearbox is at fault, and explains how that normally works. If my bad luck continued, I could ultimately learn how every part works. The point is, of course, that looking at the car when it works perfectly gives me very few clues about its internal intricacy. The faulty system gives us clues as to its normal functioning.

Of course, the car is an artefact that has been designed for specific purposes and so we can imagine how someone could come to know how each part works. The human brain and cognitive system are much more complex and it is only through research that we can work out their internal, cognitive processes. Nevertheless, it is in the same sense of looking at a damaged system that cognitive neuropsychologists study the full range of complex cognitive processes such as object recognition, reading, memory, problem solving, and so on. They have two broad and interlinked aims. The first is to explain the behaviour of brain-damaged patients in terms of damage to a previously normally functioning system. The second aim is to use information gained from studying brain-damaged patients to infer characteristics of normal cognition. So, a damaged system (e.g. impaired memory as in amnesia) can be used to create or support models of the fully-functioning system (such as Atkinson and Shiffrin's, 1968, modal model), and then these models can be used to explain the patterns of deficits seen in patients (for example, why people with amnesia have an inability to transfer information from short-term to long-term memory). However, intact cognition and the brain-damaged system go hand in hand and it is because of this that the two major goals are so closely linked.

This chapter provides a historical perspective of the field of cognitive neuropsychology and a context to the development of its use as a method within cognitive psychology. The historical evolution of knowledge and technology (such as the invention of ever-more accurate ways of looking at the brain) has itself resulted in a branching of the goals of neuropsychology. Whereas initially, perhaps for clinical reasons, simply understanding a patient's deficit was the primary aim, now studying patients has become a vital tool in the kit of the cognitive psychologist, whose aim is the explanation of cognition. This evolution of goals has itself been paralleled by more and more sophisticated methods of research, and it is these to which we shall turn in Section 4. Just as there is a range of different goals within the discipline, there are a number of different methods available, the choice of which depends on the aims of the particular neuropsychologist. To effectively conduct research they need to be aware of a range of issues and that these issues can have an impact on the choice of methods used, on the type of patient studied and on the interpretation that is feasible. Section 6 covers these issues. The chapter concludes with a brief overview of a development within the field in the 1990s, cognitive rehabilitation, which shows how information gained from research can sometimes be fed back into the rehabilitation of some aspects of a patient's condition.

2   A historical perspective

The very earliest roots of cognitive neuropsychology lie in the work of the phrenologists such as Gall and Spurzheim (1970). The **phrenologists** believed that mental 'faculties' or abilities were located in different parts of the brain, and that contours on the surface of the skull revealed the extent of an individual's abilities (see Figure 3.1). Another phrenologist, Fowler, inscribed the following on the backs of the phrenology heads that his company produced: 'For thirty years I have studied Crania and living heads from all parts of the world, and have found in every instance that there is a perfect correspondence between the conformation of the healthy skull of an individual and his known characteristics.'

For instance, Fowler believed that the 'literary, observing and knowing faculties' were situated above the right eye, that selfish properties resided under the skull above the right ear and that 'marriage, conjugality, constancy' was found near the base of the skull at the back of the head, slightly to the left of centre.

Of course, phrenology was soon discredited, but its suggestion that abilities could be functionally separated into components, and that these might be localized in different parts of the brain, is strikingly contemporary. Indeed, such suggestions are remarkably similar to the idea that cognition is modular.

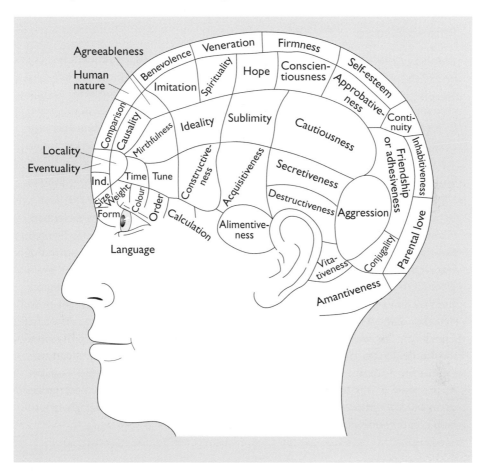

Figure 3.1   The classical phrenological head with the locations of the different mental 'faculties'

The assumption of some kind of modular organization was supported by a pivotal event in neuropsychology whose true importance was realized only many years later. In 1848, during a bizarre incident at the construction site of a Canadian railroad, Phineas Gage, one of the workers, accidentally set off an explosion that resulted in a tamping iron shooting up through his lower cheek and out of the top of his head, flying 20ft in the air before landing. Amazingly, the heat of the bar cauterized and therefore sealed the hole that it made in Gage's head. Not only did he survive, he was able to walk away from the scene and talk quite easily! Initially, it seemed that this accident had had no major harmful effects. However, with time, this previously amiable and reliable man became quite unreliable, made very bad judgments (e.g. he managed to ruin himself financially) and seemed to lose social skills. A neurologist, Harlow (1868) suggested that the damage to Phineas Gage's brain had disrupted his abilities to plan and to maintain socially accepted behaviour.

At the time, it was not possible for Harlow to investigate his ideas but, curiously, almost a hundred and fifty years later it became possible to confirm Harlow's preliminary evaluation (see Box 3.1).

3.1 — **Research study**

Phineas Gage

About 150 years after Phineas Gage's accident, a patient, EVR, underwent surgery to remove a tumour from an area in the frontal lobes just above the left eye. Because neurosurgery unavoidably involves intrusive procedures, a certain amount of brain damage is caused if the tumour is not on the surface of the brain. EVR's tumour was very deep in his frontal lobes and he was left with brain damage at the base of his left frontal lobe. Following recovery, the neurologists working with him noticed an identical change in behaviour to that seen in Phineas Gage: EVR totally immersed himself in mundane tasks, entered into risky business ventures, bankrupted himself and ultimately lost his job (Damasio, 1994).

Seeing the similarity between EVR and how Phineas Gage had been described, Hanna Damasio tried to recreate the damage that must have occurred to Phineas Gage's brain. Using Phineas Gage's skull and the original iron bar (both kept in the Harvard Medical Museum in Boston) she recreated the original shape of his brain prior to the accident. Then using a sophisticated brain-imaging system, computer simulations 'shot' the iron bar through Phineas Gage's simulated brain to determine what exact parts had been damaged in the accident (see colour Plate 8). The findings showed that the damage Phineas Gage had sustained was in the same location as EVR's. Thus, by studying EVR, it became possible to confirm Harlow's evaluation of Phineas Gage's cognitive deficits (Damasio et al., 1994). Although the main import of this study is historical, it also shows how behavioural description of individuals can combine with clinical, experimental and brain-imaging work to help create models of cognitive functioning.

Although Harlow had identified one of the first neuropsychological patients to be documented, his work did not receive substantial attention. Instead, the true roots of contemporary neuropsychology are to be found in the work of the French neurologist Paul Broca. In 1861 he treated a man who became known as 'Tan' (Broca, 1861/1965). Following a stroke (the bursting of a blood vessel in the brain), Tan had great difficulty making intelligible utterances. At most, he could produce only a few syllables at any one time, and nothing that sounded like real connected language. (He became known as Tan because of the sound of one of the syllables that he could make.) In spite of his profound inability to produce intelligible language – his aphasia – Tan was able to understand fully what was said to him. Broca proposed that a part of Tan's brain was damaged that was responsible for co-ordinating the muscle movements required for speech. Damage to this area, in spite of the vocal apparatus in the throat and mouth remaining intact, would result in the pattern of behaviour found in Tan. Post-mortem analysis of Tan's brain revealed what Broca had suspected – that damage to Tan's brain was localized to a particular area (since known as Broca's area) with the rest of his brain remaining relatively intact (Broca, 1861/1965).

In 1874, just a decade after Broca's seminal work, another neurologist, Karl Wernicke, was working with patients that exhibited the reverse of Tan's pattern of behavioural problems (Wernicke, 1874). Thus, they appeared to be able to speak fluently. They produced whole words in continuous speech that sounded superficially at least like full sentences – but had difficulties in understanding what was said to them. Although, on the surface, their speech seemed fluent, on closer examination it was found to contain many errors (such as neologisms) and was very difficult to comprehend. You can get a sense of this from a more recent example where a patient is describing a picture known as 'the cookie theft picture' (part of a diagnostic battery of tests for assessing language problems, see Figure 3.2). The patient describes it as 'Well, this is ... mother is away here working her work out o' here to get her better, but when she's looking, the two boys looking in the other part. One their small tile into her time here. She's working another time because she's getting to. So two boys working together and one is sneakin' around here, making his work an' his further funnas his time he had' (Goodglass and Kaplan, 1972, p.81). 'Funnas' is a new word or neologism.

Figure 3.2   The cookie theft picture

Source: Goodglass and Kaplan, 1972

Wernicke proposed that his patients had sustained damage to an area responsible for storing the sound patterns of words, resulting in their difficulties in comprehending speech. Post-mortem examination of one of his patients, as with Broca's patient, showed a clear specific area of damage, in the temporal lobe and slightly further back in the brain than Broca's area. Historically, this area is now known as Wernicke's area (see Figure 3.3). Although Wernicke's suggestion explained poor comprehension it didn't account for his patients' difficulties in producing fluent speech, and this issue is still not fully understood (cf Butterworth, 1979).

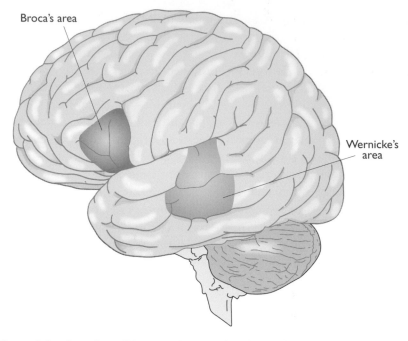

Figure 3.3 Broca's and Wernicke's areas of the brain, the locations of speech production and comprehension, respectively (a lateral view of the left side of the brain)

Although both Broca and Wernicke were neurologists (medical doctors who treated patients with brain damage), they are regarded as the fathers of modern day neuropsychology.

Broca and Wernicke were known as 'localizationalists' because they believed that certain functions were firmly localized in particular areas of the brain, i.e. speech production in Broca's area and comprehension in Wernicke's area. The result of this trend towards localizing functions anatomically was that eventually others, such as Lichteim (1885), started attempting to create models of cognitive processes, such as the production of spoken language. Due to the way these early neuropsychologists relied on visual means of describing their models in terms of boxes, representing stages, and arrows, representing information flow between them (box and arrow diagrams), they became known as the 'diagram makers'. Initially, this approach received considerable support but, over time, it attracted criticism because the models lacked clarity as to the processes involved. For example, it was postulated that there were centres that held the meanings of words and others that enabled the vocal system to produce words; however, neither centre was clearly defined. Critics of the approach have described it as 'black boxology' (since the centres are likened to black boxes that cannot be looked into). A particularly damning formulation of this criticism comes from Sutherland who defined the approach as 'the construction and ostentatious display of meaningless flow charts by psychologists as a substitute for thought' (Sutherland, 1989, p.58). As a consequence of criticism like this (levelled at the localizationalist approach since the beginning of the twentieth century) the diagram makers' approach fell into disrepute.

Although neurologists continued working with patients, it was not until the rise of the 'information-processing approach' and the birth of cognitive psychology that the ideas of the early diagram makers regained popularity. Cognitive psychology gave researchers something to put inside the black boxes that had been the diagram makers' downfall. Whereas Lichteim may have said that there was a centre for word recognition that, if damaged, would result in difficulties in understanding language, armed with ideas about information processing, computation and representation, cognitive psychologists could now attempt to describe what might happen in such centres.

Another important factor in the evolution of cognitive neuropsychology has been the development of more and more sophisticated techniques for imaging the brain's activity (such as PET, MRI and fMRI – see Chapter 2). Whereas Broca and others had to wait until their patients' deaths to be able to look at their brains, it is now possible to image the living brain. This has had a significant impact for a number of reasons. First, before the development of these techniques, researchers had to rely on simple paper and pencil tests, and then draw inferences as to the nature of the underlying brain damage (e.g. bad performance on certain subtests in an aphasia 'test' battery would imply damage in Broca's area). Now, however, it is possible to obtain images of damage in the living brain. This has a significant impact on being able to treat patients – should surgery be necessary, imaging techniques can provide surgeons with detailed anatomical pictures. Second, information concerning which parts of the brain are damaged in particular patients allows psychologists to develop more accurate models of the behaviour that they are trying to explain. Techniques such as fMRI make it possible to look at what parts of the brain are particularly active when normal healthy participants carry out tasks. This allows cognitive neuropsychologists to integrate data concerning both healthy and damaged brains (see Section 4).

Summary

- Historically, neuropsychology developed in the middle of the nineteenth century through neurologists' observations of consistent patterns of impairment in their patients.
- Early researchers were known as localizationalists because they believed that particular mental functions were situated in specific locations in the brain.
- The diagram makers, building on the ideas of the localizationalists, formulated models of mental processing in terms of 'box and arrow' diagrams.
- The demise of the diagram makers' approach gave way to renewed interest in the field of neuropsychology with the advent of cognitive psychology and the information-processing approach during the twentieth century.
- The development of more advanced techniques, such as standardized research methods and brain-imaging technology, further developed the field towards the end of the twentieth century.

3 Goals

Throughout the historical development of neuropsychology, the goals of those studying brain damage have evolved and branched. Over a century ago, neurologists were studying patients with brain damage mainly for treatment purposes. However, as the work of people like Broca and Wernicke developed, their hypotheses about what patterns of damage tell us about intact cognition were brought together by the diagram makers for the purposes of explaining mental processes. Indeed contemporary cognitive neuropsychology has a number of diverse goals, all of which depend on the type of work that the neuropsychologist is conducting. For example, a clinical neuropsychologist, who is working with a patient after they have suffered brain damage, will be interested in trying to get a good overall profile of the patient's problems and strengths, perhaps with a view to providing them with appropriate support in their day-to-day life. Someone working in rehabilitation will be interested in using a patient's preserved abilities to help them to acquire strategies for coping with impairment(s). A research neuropsychologist aims to discover what patients' problems tell us about the cognitive functions affected by brain damage, what they tell us about the normal system and what might be done to aid individual patients. In this way, the researcher would be feeding into the knowledge base of the other types of neuropsychologists. Broadly speaking, there are four main goals that define the field of neuropsychology, with different combinations of these being reflected in different kinds of neuropsychological work. These are:

- lesion localization
- assessment of a patient's deficit
- building models of normal cognition
- localization of different cognitive functions within the brain.

Neuropsychologists may need to achieve multiple goals, so that, for example, a researcher might need to assess patients before trying to build a cognitive model, and a clinician might conduct an assessment in order to determine the likely location of brain damage.

The disparity of goals illustrates the breadth of neuropsychology, but cognitive neuropsychology is just a part of a much larger field of research known as neuroscience. Neuroscience is a multidisciplinary approach that brings together a number of diverse ways of looking at the brain and cognition. These include cell anatomy, pathology, neurology, electrophysiology, neuroimaging and connectionist modelling. The difference between the approaches lies primarily in the level of neural or cognitive functioning being analyzed and the research methods employed. For example, cell anatomy is concerned with the structure and interconnections of individual cells, and neurology focuses on how the symptoms of abnormal function point towards a specific diagnosis and prognosis (e.g. stroke, degenerative illness or epilepsy); connectionist modelling on the other hand involves creating computational models of how particular systems work (such as face recognition).

3.1   Lesion localization

Before the advent of brain-imaging techniques, a neuropsychologist had to build up a picture of the site of brain damage in a patient using tests known to involve specific areas of the brain. These tests are largely 'paper and pencil' ones, designed to detect known patterns of brain damage. For instance, the Wisconsin Card Sorting Test (WCST) (Grant and Berg, 1948) was designed to assess the ability to change behaviour as a result of external feedback. The test uses a pack of cards that differ in a number of dimensions, namely shape, colour and number of objects each card depicts. The participant's task is to sort the cards according to dimensions that are chosen by the experimenter but not made explicit to the participant. The experimenter gives feedback on the sorting produced by the participant, but this may simply involve the experimenter saying whether the participant is sorting correctly or incorrectly. For example, the experimenter's initial rule may require sorting the cards by shape but then, after a number of trials, the experimenter may change the rule (e.g. to 'sort by colour') and his or her feedback would change accordingly – by responding 'incorrect' to a sort determined by shape, for example. All being well, by trial and error, the participant infers what the new dimension is on the basis of the feedback given after each trial. After the new dimension (e.g. colour) has been discovered, following a number of correct trials, the rule is changed again, perhaps to sorting by number. It is known that patients who have damage to the frontal lobes can have particular difficulties with the WCST: for instance, they might continue to sort according to a certain dimension, such as shape, even though the feedback implies that shape is now irrelevant to the rule. Consequently, a patient's poor performance on this task (defined relative to strict criteria for normal and abnormal performance) can be taken as evidence that they may have damage to the frontal lobes.

Today, localization of lesions using standardized paper and pencil tests is somewhat redundant. Neuroimaging techniques such as MRI provide accurate pictures of brain damage. However, these techniques can be costly and so if the clinician is content with a general profile of a patient's abilities (and therefore *likely* brain damage), without needing to know the precise location of lesions, then the use of paper and pencil tests may be sufficient.

Moreover, in some cases, a technique such as MRI may show no gross damage despite the patient having very clear problems. PG is a patient with very clear memory problems – a few weeks after an event he has largely forgotten it. By February, for example, he will have forgotten what he did at Christmas. Although MRI scans showed no noticeable brain damage, detailed testing involving tests specifically designed to investigate his problems, revealed a marked impairment in laying down and holding on to memories for more than a few weeks (Jansari *et al.*, 2003).

In conclusion, localization of lesions by the use of standardized tests is not as prevalent within neuropsychology as it once was. However, it remains an extremely valuable technique.

3.2   Assessment of deficit

A *clinical* neuropsychologist's main aim is to assess a patient's problem(s) by the use of whichever techniques are available, be they interviews, specific clinical tests or brain scans. Following this, if necessary, they can make a recommendation as to what types of support the patient may need.

A growing need for accurate assessment comes from the development of rehabilitation programs. Most of these attempt to circumvent a patient's main problems (e.g. an inability to lay down new long-term memories) and instead use their preserved abilities, such as preserved procedural memories (see Section 7).

3.3   Model building

Lesion localization and assessment were once the most important goals within neuropsychology, but this changed dramatically with the advent of cognitive psychology. As Selnes puts it:

> The purpose of the investigation was no longer to localize or quantify the nature of the deficit, but rather to treat the cognitive impairment as an experimental condition (induced by nature) suitable for probing specific hypotheses ...

Selnes, 2001, p.38

In this sense, the main goal became to create and test models of cognition in order to help us understand and explain complex cognitive processes, such as reading, for example.

Cognitive neuropsychology can sometimes work simply to support models that have already been developed on the basis of cognitive psychological investigations with normal participants. For example, in the 1960s mounting evidence suggested there was a difference between retaining information in memory for a few minutes and retaining it for a longer period. This sort of observation ultimately led Atkinson and Shiffrin (1968) to propose the 'modal' or 'multi-store' model of human memory in which there were different memory stores, one for short-term memory (STM) and one for long-term memory (LTM). This model was then further supported by neuropsychological evidence from the contrasting cases of patients HM and KF with a deficient LTM and a deficient STM respectively (see Section 5). (Of course, there are number of complications with this simple picture – for example, see **Rutherford, 2010**).

In other cases, neuropsychology can help to develop a model by providing novel insights into the nature of a psychological process. An example is the study of individuals who, following specific brain damage, develop an object-recognition difficulty or **agnosia**. This is a complex disorder, famously described in Oliver Sacks's *The Man Who Mistook His Wife For A Hat* (1985). The patient, although having normal vision, could not correctly identify objects. For example, when shown a glove, the patient's best attempt to name it was 'It could be a change purse ... for coins of five sizes' (Sacks, 1985).

Detailed research into patients with agnosia allowed the emergence of an understanding of how the disorder relates to normal object recognition. In a detailed case study, Humphreys and Riddoch (1987) tested a stroke patient, HJA. Although able to copy line drawings of objects, HJA was unable to *name* the same line drawings. Following a fine-grained analysis of HJA's visual recognition and drawing abilities, Humphreys and Riddoch (1987) suggested that there is a stage in the object recognition process at which visual information is 'integrated' into one coherent representation. Their suggestion is that HJA cannot do this integration and so although able to copy line drawings, the visual information required for this did not allow him to recognize the object. Another patient – JF – was also unable to name objects that he could draw perfectly well, but in JF's case he didn't have any difficulty in miming the use of the object (Lhermitte and Beauvois, 1973). This led to the conclusion that it is possible to access semantic information concerning an object and yet still be unable to name it. Without these neuropsychological findings (concerning integration of visual information and access to semantic information being part of a long chain of processes required to name an object), it would be extremely difficult to identify these different processing stages.

A further example of a novel finding that helps to explain normal cognitive processes is provided by the rare **split brain syndrome**. This arises from a drastic surgical procedure, pioneered in 1965 by Bogen and Vogel, to alleviate intractable epilepsy (Bogen and Vogel, 1965). The procedure, which is carried out only in extreme circumstances, aims to prevent epilepsy spreading from one cerebral hemisphere to another. It involves severing the tract of fibres, known as the corpus callosum (see Figure 3.4), which connects the two hemispheres, with the result that they then operate in relative isolation from one another. Because the procedure (called a commissurotomy) is carried out so rarely, there are only about fifty split brain patients in the world.

Figure 3.4   The position of the corpus callosum. A sagittal view of the brain

Due to the pioneering work of researchers such as Sperry and Gazzaniga (e.g. Gazzaniga *et al.*, 1962; Sperry and Gazzaniga, 1967) we now know that a patient with a split brain shows a number of characteristics that together form a syndrome of problems. A classic one is known as **astereognosis**, which manifests itself as an inability to identify an object that is held in the left hand without being able to look at it. This can be demonstrated using an experiment in which the subject can only feel a range of objects but is prevented from seeing them (see Figure 3.5 overleaf).

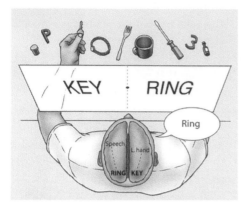

Figure 3.5 In this Gazzaniga *et al.* experiment, a split brain patient is prevented from seeing what is held in the left hand and, because the connection between the speech-oriented left hemisphere and the somatosensory cortex of the right hemisphere is cut, the subject is unable to identify the object

Source: Gazzaniga *et al.*, 1998, p.331

This work has allowed scientists to confirm the idea that information from the left hand about what an object feels like, its size, texture, etc., is processed initially by the right hemisphere and that information from the right hand is processed by the left hemisphere. That is, for motor control and processing of tactile information, the brain's organization is **contralateral** – each of the hemispheres is in control of, or processes information from, the *opposite* side of the body. As a result, information deriving from the left hand about a small hard object that has a big cavity in it as well as a section on the side for holding it (such as a cup) will firstly be processed by the somatosensory cortex in the right hemisphere. Although this hemisphere can represent the object in terms of how it feels, its name is thought to be inaccessible because this linguistic information is represented in the left hemisphere. That is, ordinarily, sensory information about the cup needs to be passed to the left hemisphere, via the corpus callosum, for the name to be accessed. Since this tract of connections has been cut in split brain patients, such transmission of information is not possible – sensory information is 'trapped' in the right hemisphere and the patient cannot name the object! However, as soon as the cup is put in the right hand, the patient can access its name because information from this hand goes to the somatosensory cortex in the left hemisphere. This representation of the physical feel of the object can then be used to access its name, since the linguistic information is also in the left hemisphere. Curiously, then, when a split brain patient cannot see an object, his or her right hand can 'name' it even though their left hand cannot! This sort of neuropsychological finding helped to support existing theories of specialization of the two hemispheres for which scientists already had some evidence. Therefore, it is now known that motor control of one part of the body is controlled by the contralateral hemisphere, that the left hemisphere is specialized for linguistic processing whilst the right specializes in spatial thought and that most of the information flow between these areas happens cortically through the corpus callosum.

Other work on split brain patients has provided novel findings. For example, Luck *et al.* have looked at whether attentional processes are split between the two hemispheres or whether each hemisphere has its own attentional system; their findings suggest the latter (Luck *et al.*, 1994). Ramachandran *et al.* have looked at which types of cognitive information are transferred between the cerebral cortices via the corpus callosum and which types are transferred subcortically via other pathways that are spared in the commissurotomy procedure (Ramachandran *et al.*,1986). Their work has suggested that 'lower order' cognitive information such as shape and motion can be transferred subcortically, whereas 'higher order' information such as language and meaning is transferred cortically. Without information gained from split brain patients, this kind of insight into normal cognitive processing would be difficult to obtain. Specifically, the findings from split brain patients provide valuable information concerning the extent of hemispheric specialization and the cortical and sub-cortical flow of information between the hemispheres. In summary, neuropsychology as a whole can provide a vital link in the chain involved in building models of normal cognition.

3.4   Localization of function

Although the early workers in the field, such as Broca, Wernicke and Lichteim, were attempting to identify specific areas of the brain as being involved in certain processes, this is just one possible goal of cognitive neuropsychology. Indeed, many other researchers feel that the need to explain the nature of cognitive processes is more pressing than the question of where in the brain they occur. And still others acknowledge the issue of function localization but separate this from the question of the cognitive processing involved. For example, although there exist complex neuropsychological models of face- and object-recognition, the emphasis in many of the models is on the types of representations involved and the flow of information processing, rather than on the role of specific locations in the brain (e.g. Bruce and Young, 1986; Humphreys *et al.*, 1988).

Finally cognitive neuroscientists who use neuropsychology as one of their range of methods are concerned with trying to work out *how* a cognitive process works as well as *where* in the brain it primarily occurs and use data from patients, normal controls, animal studies, molecular studies, etc. It should be noted that whereas the early localizationalists such as Broca and Wernicke may have believed that certain areas were solely involved in particular functions, cognitive function is now known generally to involve many areas of the brain working *together* (much like the earlier example of the car working as a whole). Cognitive neuroscientists simply suggest that there are certain areas that are at the *end-point* of a long, processing pathway for particular functions. So for example, the whole of the visual system needs to be functioning well to recognize people's faces but Damasio *et al.*, suggest that the **right temporal pole** (an area of the brain just below the right temple) is the most critical component (Damasio *et al.*, 1996). Similarly, work in the field of memory is now attempting to work out the exact role of the (left) temporal lobe and, in particular, a specific area within it known as the perirhinal cortex in the formation of memories. This work attempts to address both the types of representation involved at different points in cognitive processing and also where the various stages of processing occur (e.g. Aggleton and Brown, 1999). Figure 3.6 shows a preliminary understanding of the critical areas for a range of cognitive functions.

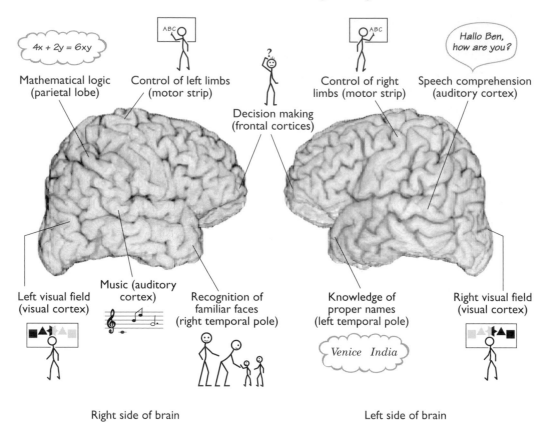

Figure 3.6   The different areas of specialization in the left and right hemispheres of the brain

In spite of the variety of positions researchers take with regard to function localization, it could be said to be an *ultimate* aim of neuropsychology since, as well as giving an understanding of how and where different cognitive information is processed, localization would allow us to make predictions about the consequences of brain damage. For instance, neurosurgeons wanting to remove a tumour or the focus of epileptic seizures need to know that their invasive surgery will have minimal detrimental effects. Knowing that language processing generally, but not always, takes place in the left hemisphere now means that a pre-operative test (known as an amytal abreaction) is conducted on patients who are about to undergo surgery. If the test confirms the processing of language in the left hemisphere, the surgeon(s) will attempt to spare the language areas of the left hemisphere as much as possible.

Summary

- There are four main goals of cognitive neuropsychology: identification of localization of a lesion; assessment of the deficits suffered by a patient; creation of cognitive models; and finally identification of localization of function.
- The goals of neuropsychology depend on the role of the neuropsychologist – workers in the clinical, research and rehabilitation fields all have slightly different goals.
- Localization of a lesion was one of the earliest goals of neuropsychology since knowing where a patient has brain damage has an important impact on understanding their deficits.
- Assessment of deficit is important for gaining a profile of the impaired and intact abilities following brain damage and is the main goal of clinical neuropsychology.
- The building of cognitive models is the main goal of researchers who utilize information gained from studying damaged systems to propose accounts of cognitive processing.
- Localization of function is related to the early localizationalist approach but is now an advanced goal where the information gained from a number of related disciplines within neuroscience can help identify where in the brain different aspects of processing occur.

4   Techniques used for assessing and studying brain damage

Reflecting the fact that different neuropsychologists pursue slightly different goals, these are a variety of methods in use within neuropsychology.

4.1   Standardized testing

Clinicians tend to draw on an extensive range of 'standardized' tests that have been carefully constructed to tap very specific functions. For instance, there are tests that assess memory functioning (e.g. the Wechsler Memory Scale-III, or WMS-III), general intellectual functioning (e.g. the Wechsler Adult Intelligence Scale, or WAIS) and visuo-spatial abilities (e.g. the Birmingham Object Recognition Battery, or BORB). These may be short single tests or involve a large number of subtests aimed at tapping different subcomponents of the particular cognitive function being investigated.

One of the most important and useful aspects of standardized clinical tests is that they will have been created with graded difficulty and the performance for a large range of participants is published with each test. These published 'norms' can be analysed separately by whatever demographic variables are thought to be important in the performance of the task. For example, if age is thought to affect scores, then norms will be published for different age groups and a patient's performance can be compared with those from the same age group. Some tests (e.g. the Visual Object and Space Perception test, or VOSP) also provide data for the performance of large groups of people with particular kinds of brain damage, allowing the clinician to see immediately if a patient's score falls within the range typical of one of these groups. The clinical neuropsychologist may then use the information from standardized tests in reporting to other health care professionals involved in the patient's welfare, on the basis of which treatment or rehabilitation regimes may be devised.

4.2 Experimental neuropsychology

As mentioned above, the experimental neuropsychologist assesses patients in order to probe particular theories of cognition: the patient becomes a test-bed for ideas. There are five main methods that are available for this purpose. These are:

- the use of standardized tests (as above)

- employing paradigms already used in cognitive psychology

- designing new techniques aimed at looking at specific issues in a patient or group of patients

- neuroimaging (see Chapter 2) and

- connectionist modelling (see Reading 1, 'Connectionism' by Martin Le Voi which you will find on the DD303 website).

As we will see, these are not mutually exclusive – it is possible to use a variety of methods in combination. However, some methods may not be available for a number of reasons.

Patients are often initially assessed using whatever standardized tests are available. This allows the neuropsychologist to build up a picture of the patient's impairments and their intact abilities. Following this initial assessment, paradigms that are already used in cognitive psychology can be used to probe particular issues. A classic example involves the identification of separate short-term and long-term memory processes (termed the 'free recall paradigm'). Normal healthy participants, when asked to remember a list of words and then tested for immediate recall, will generate a classic U-shaped curve known as the 'serial position curve' (SPC). The curve shows the probability of someone recalling a word as a function of its position in the list, and has three main portions: very good recall of the first few items (known as 'primacy'), very good recall of the last few items (known as 'recency') and intermediate to lower recall of the items not at the extremes (known as the 'asymptote').

It has been suggested that primacy arises because early items in the list have been successfully transferred to LTM whilst recency reflects the fact that items are still being held in STM. Mid-list items are poorly recalled because they are less likely to have been successfully transferred to LTM (because of concentration on the early items) and will have been displaced from STM by later items. If this explanation is correct, then it would be predicted that patients unable to transfer information from STM to LTM would not show all three portions of the curve. This is exactly what was found by Baddeley and Warrington (1970) – their participants with amnesia showed a SPC in which there was little evidence of primacy, whilst the amount of recency was indistinguishable from that of non-brain-damaged controls (see Figure 3.7). This robust neuropsychological finding helped to support an influential

Figure 3.7 Amnesic patients show little evidence of remembering early items in a list (primacy) but their recall of more recent items is identical to that of normal patients

Source: Baddeley and Warrington, 1970

cognitive theory of the separation of different memory stores (Atkinson and Shiffrin, 1968) (though for further discussion, for example, see **Rutherford, 2010**).

As well as using tasks such as the free recall paradigm described above, an important task of the neuropsychological experimenter is to be able to create tasks that are specific to the patient under investigation. By the very nature of investigative work, new issues are being explored and therefore the use of standardized clinical tests and already existing experimental tests will not always be appropriate. For example, Jansari *et al.* tested an epileptic patient PG who complained of memory problems (Jansari *et al.*, 2003). His SPC was normal, however, as was his performance on standardized clinical memory tests. This apparently normal clinical profile in the face of complaints of memory problems led to a detailed case study of his LTM. It is thought that in the normally functioning brain, a neurobiological consolidation process within LTM gradually strengthens memory traces of past events, allowing them to be later recalled. It was felt that PG's epilepsy might be disrupting this consolidation. The standardized clinical tests were designed to assess the *transfer* of information from STM to LTM but not the strength of the resulting long-term memories. Now it is well known that repeated recall of a particular piece of information (a memory) strengthens its representation in LTM. If PG's memory problems arose because information in his LTM was represented less strongly than normal, then repeated recall should reduce the problem. After having been presented with stories for later recall, his recall was poor for stories he was only ever allowed to recall once (ranging from a day to four weeks after initial presentation). However, for stories he was allowed to recall more often, his recall matched that of normal healthy controls (see Figure 3.8).

Figure 3.8 By repeatedly recalling stories, PG was able to improve his recall of the story to the level of normal subjects

Source: Jansari *et al.*, 2003

Experimental neuropsychologists will often, if possible, use some sort of brain-imaging technique (such as CAT or MRI scans). These techniques yield images of the structure of the brain and can reveal any gross lesions (or areas of damage). More sophisticated techniques (such as PET, fMRI and SPECT) can image the brain while it is performing cognitive tasks to see which parts are utilized for different tasks (see Chapter 2). For example, in two studies, Damasio and colleagues used a number of functional brain-imaging techniques to identify which parts of the brain were most active when normal controls were answering questions on different types of information. They found specific areas associated with knowledge for people, animals and tools. They then divided a group of brain-damaged patients with object-recognition difficulties into three sub-groups, depending on which of the same three classes of objects they had most difficulty recognizing. Finally, they tried to identify areas of brain damage that were common within each group of patients. They found that the patients had lesions in the same areas that were most active when normal controls viewed the same objects (see colour Plate 9). Damage to each of these areas therefore resulted in the differing behavioural patterns in recognition found in the patients (Damasio *et al.*, 1996; Tranel *et al.*, 1997).

Although brain-imaging can be a powerful and useful technique, it does have limitations. It is expensive and not readily available to all researchers. Moreover, with some patients, such as PG mentioned earlier, some scanning techniques reveal no physical or functional problems despite the patient exhibiting a behavioural impairment. Finally, it is even possible to question the usefulness of brain-imaging for clarifying cognitive processes; however, it is beyond the scope of this chapter to go into such debates.

A further method that has gained much momentum within the field is that of cognitive modelling (of which connectionist modelling is one approach). The basic aim of cognitive modelling is to build models (using computer programs) that behave in the same way as humans (see Reading 2, 'Symbolic modelling', which you will find on the DD303 website). Having developed an account of say, face recognition, perhaps drawing on a combination of all the other available methods, a cognitive modeller will then seek to program its various aspects in a cognitive model. The model can then be tested by providing it with input and comparing the output it produces to normal human performance. If the system successfully mimics human behaviour (in that it provides correct answers when humans do, and incorrect answers when humans also make errors), then there is some justification for believing that normal cognitive processes are similar. Of course, there is no guarantee that the model actually functions in the same way as the normal human system (Coltheart, 2001); cognitive modelling simply suggests plausible mechanisms and processes.

One of the reasons this method has become popular in neuropsychology is that, with some models, it is possible to 'lesion' the model by damaging some of its components. In effect, this creates an analogue to the brain damage that disrupts parts of a patient's normally functioning system. The lesioned model can now be tested by comparing it with the performance of neuropsychological patients. This method has proved very successful in certain parts of cognition. For example, Farah and McClelland (1991) created a model of the problems experienced by certain patients with agnosia (object-recognition difficulty) such as their having more difficulty in naming living things (e.g. animals) than non-living things (e.g. types of furniture), a finding first documented by Warrington and Shallice (1984). Similarly, Coltheart (1987) has tried to recreate in a model the reading errors exhibited by patients with different forms of acquired dyslexia (see Section 6.4 below).

In summary, therefore, there is a wide range of methods available to the experimental neuropsychologist. The choice will depend on a large number of factors, including the type of patient being studied, the specificity of their deficit, the range of models already in existence that might explain (parts of) their behaviour and the availability of techniques such as neuroimaging and cognitive modelling.

An important point here is that just as the different neuropsychological methods are not in competition with one another, the same argument holds for the choice of a neuropsychological approach as opposed to other approaches to studying cognition. Neuropsychology is a method that *complements* and works together with other methods rather than being an *alternative*. A classic example of how different approaches can complement one another is found in the development of models of face processing. Early studies using introspective diary methods gave an insight into the general stages of face processing, resulting in Young *et al.*'s functional model of face processing (Young *et al.*, 1985). Experimental work, first on normal and then brain-damaged individuals, then led to the components of this model being expanded and clarified in the Bruce and Young (1986) model. Finally, problems with this latter model led to Burton *et al.* creating IAC, a connectionist model able to account for most of the findings to date (Burton *et al.*, 1990). For further information see **Pike and Brace (2010)**.

Summary

- The techniques used by neuropsychologists depend on their particular goal in working with a patient.
- Assessment is carried out using standardized tests for which published data on the performance of a variety of participant groups is available. This allows the clinician to evaluate the extent of problems with different areas of cognition.
- Experimental research involves a range of techniques including both established tasks and new paradigms specially created for working with particular patients or patient groups.
- Neuroimaging has already established itself as a vital tool in research, though there may be some cases where it is unable to shed light on deficits in patients that are manifest behaviourally.
- A further method of research involves implementing proposed models using connectionist architectures, which allow the plausibility of the models to be tested.

5   Dissociations and double dissociations

Having used various techniques to evaluate a patient's intact abilities and deficits, the next task of the neuropsychologist is to make inferences from the evidence gained. How do neuropsychologists infer the existence of separate cognitive functions within the brain (e.g. language being separate from memory)? How can they infer that each function is composed of separate processes (e.g. within face processing, different paths for recognition of faces and recognition of the emotion in the face)? Neuropsychologists look to see which cognitive problems tend to occur together and, more importantly, which ones can occur in the absence of other problems. For example, it has been repeatedly observed that certain patients retain an ability to remember items for a few minutes but lose their ability to remember the same information for longer periods (e.g. patient HM reported by Scoville and Milner, 1957). The conclusion is that two types of memory are involved and that, in these patients, the two kinds of memory **dissociate** from one another – it is possible to lose one whilst retaining the other intact. This sort of **dissociation** was used to support early models of memory such as the modal model proposed by Atkinson and Shiffrin (1968) which has separate STM and LTM components.

However, it can be argued that a single dissociation does not entitle us to postulate independent processes. There could be a simpler explanation. For instance, suppose there were just one memory system, and that in that system the more effort you put into remembering information, the more likely it was that you would retain it for longer periods. That is, more 'effort' is required to retain information for a few hours than it is to do so for just a few minutes (see Figure 3.9(a)). Now if brain damage reduced the cognitive effort a person was able to make, this might have little impact on the ability to retain information for short periods but a large impact on retention over longer periods (see Figure 3.9(b)). The situation would be similar to having had a heavy illness for a few weeks, resulting in easy exercise such as walking being possible but more strenuous activities such as running or swimming proving more challenging. The pattern of memory loss would be as in HM and other amnesic persons but this would not be evidence for separate STM and LTM stores or processes.

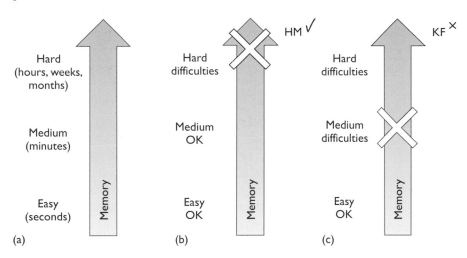

Figure 3.9 (a) In a hypothetical 'unitary' memory system, more 'effort' is required to retain information over longer periods; (b) Damage to the hypothetical unitary system is most likely to affect performance on more difficult memory tasks. This could explain cases such as HM who have an inability to remember events that happened more than a few minutes ago; (c) If the hypothetical unitary system is more severely damaged resulting in problems with memory for information heard a few minutes ago, it is impossible to explain how a patient such as KF can still be able to remember what happened an hour, a week or many months ago

Is this explanation in terms of 'difficulty' to be preferred to one that invokes (at least) two separate processes? What if a patient was found who has no problems with remembering information from a few weeks ago but cannot repeat back a list of six single digit numbers after ten seconds? This type of performance could not be explained in terms of 'difficulty' because if someone can do the 'difficult' task of remembering from weeks ago, then they should be able to do the 'easy' task (Figure 3.9(c)). However, such a patient has been reported. Following an injury, KF has had problems with certain aspects of STM but his LTM is normal (Shallice and Warrington, 1970). These contrasting patterns of impairment shown by HM and KF, where HM has impaired LTM but intact STM whilst KF has impaired STM but intact LTM, is known as a **double dissociation**. This type of finding is extremely useful for neuropsychologists since it seems strongly to imply the existence of two separate systems either of which can be damaged. Such a double dissociation allows researchers to say that (at least to some degree) STM and LTM are separate processes. The existence of further double dissociations then allows for further fractionation of memory (Figure 3.10 overleaf).

Figure 3.10 Conceptual 'memory tree' that can be created from evidence of dissociations and double dissociations

Other clear examples of double dissociation occur in face processing, between recognition of someone's identity and recognition of the emotion on their face (e.g. Adolphs *et al.*, 1994), and in reading, between phonological and surface dyslexia (e.g. Coltheart, 1987). It should be noted that, although double dissociations are usually found *between* patients, they can also be found *within* the processing of one patient. For example, a patient DB has a condition known as **blindsight** – there are areas of his vision in which he is effectively blind, yet he processes at least some visual information from that area, albeit without awareness; a case of 'seeing but not being aware of it' (Weiskrantz, 1986, 1987). In a complex experiment comparing this area of blindness with areas of intact processing, a double dissociation was found between his ability to make judgements about low-level visual processing and his ability to accurately detect shapes (a higher-level visual task). Within-subject double dissociations have also been reported in patients with neglect (Beschin *et al.*, 2000; Pisella *et al.*, 2002).

Generally speaking, double dissociations are extremely useful in the development of cognitive models of normal functions. However, there are some who advise caution when interpreting such findings. For example, Young *et al.* (1993) list a number of problems including:

1   Patients who show double dissociations are often studied in different laboratories and with methods that are not standardized. So different stimuli may have been used to demonstrate their problems. For example, in the field of object recognition some researchers (e.g. Warrington and Shallice, 1984) have reported patients who have much greater problems recognizing living things than non-living things whilst others (e.g. Sacchett and Humphreys, 1992) have reported the reverse case. This has led many (e.g. McCarthy and Warrington, 1990) to argue that the semantic system is split along categorical lines with a major subdivision between living and non-living objects. However, critics (e.g. Gaffan and Heywood, 1993) have argued that the double dissociation may be an artefact of the different studies having used different materials for testing. As a counter to this possibility, Hillis and Caramazza (1991) have shown a clear double dissociation between two patients, tested at similar times, in the same laboratory and on the same material.

2   How a deficit or dissociation in a patient is judged can be a highly subjective matter. For example, imagine a person who performs *below normal* on two tasks but better on task A than on task B. If a second patient is found, who is also below normal on both tasks but shows the reverse pattern (i.e. better performance on task B than on A), can these two patterns be interpreted as a double dissociation? Some argue that it is necessary for at least one of the two functions to be relatively intact in each patient to justify the use of the data from the two patients to claim a double dissociation. In this hypothetical example, since neither patient shows intact performance on either of the two tasks, it can be suggested that the evidence is not strong enough to prove a double dissociation.

3   'Normal' performance on a task does not necessarily mean normal cognitive functioning since a person may be using a compensatory strategy not found in people with an intact cognitive system (see next section). For example, Humphreys and Riddoch's (1987) patient HJA seemed to be able to copy line drawings well, implying an intact ability to perceive the drawings properly. However, closer inspection showed that his drawing strategy was very laborious and piecemeal with different parts of the object being selectively reproduced, rather than what one might expect if HJA perceived the object as a complete whole. It is therefore important to ensure that a patient is tested in a variety of ways to ensure that seemingly normal performance is being produced in a normal fashion.

Moreover, researchers have questioned the extent to which a double dissociation does imply the existence of separate systems. Glymour (1994), for example, argues that a double dissociation could arise from a single process containing distinct stages that can sustain damage independently from one another. Juola and Plunkett (1998) describe the results of damaging a connectionist model, which they argue implements a 'single route, single mechanism'. Damage nevertheless gave rise to the appearance of a double dissociation. Again, the implication is that double dissociations cannot be taken to necessarily imply the existence of separate processing systems.

Clearly it is important to observe caution when interpreting dissociations and double dissociations. Since these interpretations can have major theoretical implications, it is also important that patients are tested as rigorously as possible. As Ellis and Young say, it 'would be unwise to regard the search for double dissociations as some sort of royal road to understanding the structure of the mind' (1988, p.5).

Summary

- If one cognitive ability is impaired in a patient (e.g. language) whilst leaving another intact (e.g. memory), these two abilities are said to **dissociate** and to possibly constitute separate cognitive processes.
- It is possible to explain some cases of single dissociation in terms of a unitary system rather than having to invoke two separate processes. In this simpler

system, the more effortful aspects of processing (e.g. remembering events from many years ago) can be impaired whilst leaving more basic aspects (e.g. retaining five digits in memory for a minute) intact. If such an explanation is possible, researchers should adopt it on grounds of simplicity.

- However, if two patients are found, one of whom is impaired on task A (e.g. ability to recognize emotion shown in a face) but has no problems with task B (e.g. ability to recognize faces) whilst another patient shows the reverse pattern (impaired on B but intact on A), these two abilities are said to show a **double dissociation**. A finding like this can be strong evidence for the existence of separate cognitive processes.

- Nevertheless, there are many caveats to be borne in mind concerning the interpretation of double dissociations.

6 Important issues for cognitive neuropsychological research

Whatever the main aim of the neuropsychologist, be it conducting a clinical assessment or empirical research, he or she needs to be aware of a number of issues when working with patients with brain damage. If the patient is being assessed for research purposes, it will be necessary to consider how representative they are of the normal population, since the aim of research is to generalize to intact cognitive processes. Similarly, in trying to compare patients, the extent to which it is possible to compare individuals with different brains, and whose brain damage could differ either only subtly or greatly, needs to be given careful thought. In drawing inferences from the nature of damaged systems to normal intact processing, assumptions need to be made carefully. Similarly, it needs to be considered that the brain may show some changes in recovering from damage. An important question when conducting empirical research concerns the choice and number of patients in a study – is it better to conduct a fine-grained analysis of one patient or to study a group of patients that appear to have a common deficit? Finally, brain damage early in life, when the brain is still forming, can have different consequences from damage that occurs to a fully formed brain. So, it is important to consider the period of the patient's life during which they suffered brain damage, as this can significantly alter the interpretation placed on findings.

6.1 The Martian among us

A central assumption of neuropsychology is that, before brain damage, the patient's cognitive system worked in essentially the same way as any other person's. If this is the case, then it may be possible to infer from the patient's damaged system how the normal intact system functions. However, what if the assumption proves unfounded and even before brain damage the patient had an unusual cognitive system, quite unlike the rest of the population? This is what Caramazza (1986) describes as the problem of the 'Martian among us'. If the patient has an abnormal cognitive system to begin with, then any inferences drawn from their damaged system to the nature of the normal cognitive system would be unsound. As a result, one of the principal goals of neuropsychology, to investigate the functioning of the normal intact system, would be undermined. This, of course, is a serious issue, especially since it is not possible to go back and check that the patient's intact system was indeed normal prior to brain damage. It is for this reason that single case studies need to be extremely detailed and rigorous and are usually followed up by investigating other patients.

6.2   Comparing brains

One way in which scientific research moves forward is through the replication and extension of studies that are deemed important. In the case of cognitive neuropsychology, one could test out theories suggested by the study of one patient on another patient with similar problems. However, even if two patients were to show similar behavioural profiles, would that mean that their brains were similar, with the same size and extent of brain lesions? Even small differences in the size of lesions can produce subtle behavioural differences that may impact significantly on task performance.

However, even the brains of healthy identical twins show differences in structure, so caution should be applied when comparing the brains of patients (see Figure 3.11 overleaf). One need not be a specialist in brain anatomy to see that the two brains in Figure 3.11 look similar but are far from *identical*. If this is the case for genetically identical individuals, then the brains of patients who are unrelated to one another are likely to have differed prior to damage.

Even if two brains were identical, nature or even neurosurgery does not result in 'clean lesions' restricted to distinct well-defined regions. A blood vessel bursting may result in widespread damage affecting a number of different areas. For example, researchers may be interested in production of spoken language which, as described above, involves Broca's area in the frontal lobes. They might therefore wish to study a patient who has suffered stroke damage in this area. However, the patient may also have experienced damage to adjacent cortical areas. The result is that, as well as difficulty in producing coherent speech, the patient may have other cognitive problems. Therefore, the patient's speech problems could arise solely because of damage to Broca's area, or solely because of damage to neighbouring areas (perhaps because that interrupts the flow of information to Broca's area), or because of a combination of both types of damage. If this sort of issue can cause complications when studying one damaged brain, it is therefore not surprising that comparing two patients who may both have differing damage that extends beyond Broca's area can greatly compound the problem. As a result, neuropsychologists need to carefully consider all of the damage suffered by a patient rather than that which is the focus of their research. Again, this requires thorough analysis of the patient's intact and impaired abilities.

6.3   Subtractivity

An important assumption of cognitive neuropsychology is that a damaged system is just the same as a normal one but with certain modules or processing systems removed or damaged. This assumption of **subtractivity** then makes it possible to conceptually 'fractionate' the cognitive system, as shown in Box 3.2.

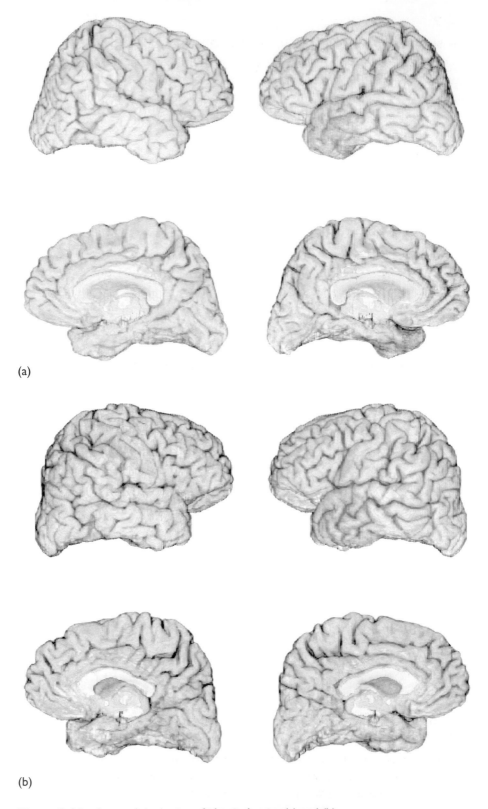

(a)

(b)

Figure 3.11 Scans of the brains of identical twins (a) and (b)

3.2 ——————————————— Methods

A simplified example of the fractionation of cognition

Assume, for sake of argument that, by the use of double dissociations and the study of many patients, it has been possible to infer the existence of five main components of the cognitive system. You could imagine that these five are problem solving, reading, object recognition, face recognition and memory, but such details are not necessary – the example is only illustrative. If cognition had been seen intuitively as one big system, it would then be subdivided, conceptually, into five modules (Figure 3.12). (Of course, there have been many detailed and complex arguments concerning the subdivision or fractionation of cognition – for present purposes we need only imagine that these have resulted in the five subdivisions shown.)

Figure 3.12   A hypothetical subdivision of the cognitive system into five major components

Researchers working with patients with memory problems have repeatedly found that, following brain damage, some patients can hold onto information for a few seconds but cannot retain it for longer. Similarly, as mentioned previously, there are some (very rare) patients who cannot remember a short string of digits for a few seconds but nonetheless have a perfectly normal ability to lay down long-term memories. If we ignore complications (such as discussed in **Rutherford, 2010**) then the double dissociation can be taken as evidence for a further sub-division of the memory component into STM and LTM (Figure 3.13).

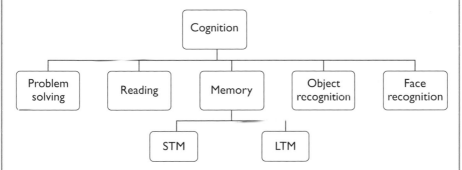

Figure 3.13   Double dissociations could provide evidence for the further sub-division of memory into two stores, STM and LTM

Further research on patient HM showed that he could learn to perform tasks such as the Tower of Hanoi puzzle without becoming aware of having done the task before. Since learning the task might span weeks or months, knowledge of how to perform the task has clearly become part of LTM. Indeed, researchers such as Cohen and Squire (1980) proposed that LTM consists of two general types of memory, memory for facts and events, known as **declarative** memory and memory for skills, known as **procedural** memory (see Figure 3.14). Work with amnesic patients such as HM suggests they have experienced damage to their declarative memory, but not their procedural memory.

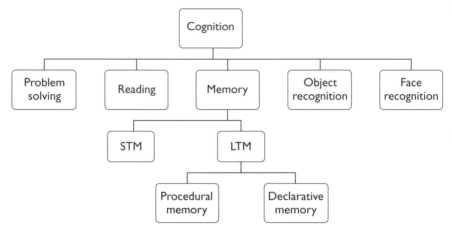

Figure 3.14 Dissociations, as in HM, between (a) the learning and long-term retention of new skills and (b) conscious knowledge of learning those skills, allows LTM to be further sub-divided into procedural and declarative memory

By careful observation of double dissociations, it is possible to reason that cognition is fractionated into many different functional components. However, note that at each step, the assumption of subtractivity is made. That is, a patient may be interpreted as having experienced damage to one or more processing systems, but it is assumed that other systems are undamaged and that the remainder of the system operates normally.

By studying a variety of patients, it is possible to infer further subdivisions. For example, Baddeley and colleagues (e.g. Baddeley *et al.*, 1975; Baddeley and Hitch, 1977) have shown how it is possible to replace what was previously thought of as STM with a more complex model of working memory, which contains a number of different subsystems (see, for example, **Hitch, 2010**). In this way, by working meticulously on different patients with different types of problem and assuming that, with each one, one or more aspect of the overall cognitive system has been damaged, a model of the entire system can be created. This then meets one of the goals of neuropsychology, which is to use information from brain-damaged patients to infer the structure of the normal intact system. At the same time, deficits seen subsequently in patients can be used to evaluate the inferred system by seeing if their particular pattern of deficit can be explained via the subtraction of particular components. Finally, when it is discovered that not all aspects of the system have been damaged – for example, that in people with amnesia procedural memory is intact – it is possible to try to use these undamaged processing systems in rehabilitation (a point to which we return in the next section).

6.4   Plasticity

Through applying the assumption of subtractivity, successful and complex models of normal cognition have been developed. However, it is important to note that the assumption may not always be strictly valid because of the plasticity of the brain. **Plasticity** refers to the ability of the brain to repair itself both at the neuronal and cognitive level. As Rose and Johnson (1996) state:

> Far from being fixed, unchangeable and static, we now know that the brain is a dynamic and interactive organ, constantly changing in terms of cellular activity, neural circuitry and transmitter chemistry in response to demands placed upon it.

For example, it is known from work on animal brains that neurons lost in lesions can be replaced. Also, under certain circumstances, the normal function of an area of the brain that has been damaged can 'move' to another undamaged area. For example, babies that suffer severe strokes in their left hemisphere (where language is *normally* processed) can nevertheless sometimes develop language processing in their right hemisphere (Bates, 1998).

   In the adult brain, this nearly complete switch of language from the left to the right hemisphere is not found. However, if even *some* cognitive functions can move to another intact part of the brain, then the assumption of subtractivity does not strictly apply, and so inferences from patients to the normal cognitive system are not strictly valid.

   Consider the following use of subtractivity. Imagine that, by studying normal control participants and patients with different types of dyslexia, each having suffered damage to their left hemisphere, researchers have identified six sub-components to the reading system that we can label A to F (see Figure 3.15). Furthermore, imagine it is claimed that, following extensive damage to this system (which we can illustrate in Figure 3.16 as affecting E and F), some aspects of reading begin to utilize an entirely different processing system. We can depict this 'new' system as sub-component X in Figure 3.16.

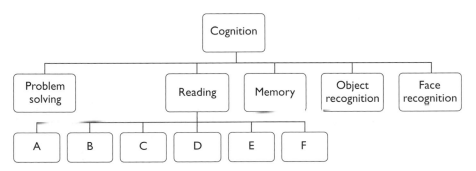

Figure 3.15   Imagine that researchers have identified six sub-components to the reading system (A–F)

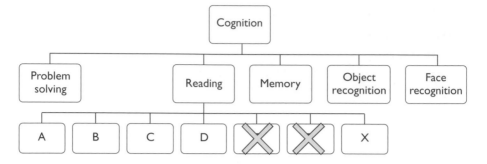

Figure 3.16 Imagine that, following damage to the hypothetical sub-components E and F, the individual's brain begins to use a different processing system for some aspects of reading (X)

In fact, in the case of deep dyslexia, just this kind of claim has been made. In particular, it has been argued that, subsequent to brain damage, some aspects of reading begin to occur using a processing system that plays no part in the normal reading system (Coltheart, 1987). It is beyond the scope of this chapter to give a full account of the theory, but it is claimed that there is a complex interaction between this 'new' right hemisphere processing system and those aspects of reading that are still intact in the left hemisphere. This interaction is thought to be suboptimal resulting in a cluster of consistent reading errors in deep dyslexic patients that include semantic errors (e.g. reading the word 'SWORD' as 'dagger'), visual errors (e.g. reading 'WHILE' as 'white') and difficulties in reading words of low imageability (e.g. having more problems reading 'JUSTICE' than 'TABLE'). This theory of deep dyslexia involving a right hemisphere processing system is one that is still under debate.

For present purposes, however, it is important to note that the theory illustrates a difficulty for the assumption of subtractivity. Notice that this 'new' processing system (akin to process X in Figure 3.16) is not representative of the normal reading system (which, in Figure 3.15, comprises modules A to F). Hence, deep dyslexia might not reflect the operation of a normal system with certain components damaged, but the operation of a non-normal system. To date, there is very little evidence that the right hemisphere becomes involved in normal intact reading. As a result, because of the possibility of this kind of plasticity, researchers need to apply caution when assuming subtractivity.

6.5 Single-case versus group studies

Conventionally, experimental psychology proceeds by measuring differences and subjecting these to statistical analysis. Such analyses indicate the likelihood of obtaining such differences by chance, through sampling. Often, a large number of participants are studied in order to ensure generalizability. However, in neuropsychological research, it may be impossible to find more than a few patients with a rare condition, so preventing the use of group designs. Even if it were possible to find a group of such patients, problems can arise due to the heterogeneity of brain damage in the group. The result is that the neuropsychologist is often faced with a decision as to whether to study a single patient in depth or to try to use a group of patients all with the same cognitive deficit. Let us look first at some of the difficulties associated with each approach, and then consider the criteria that a researcher might use in arriving at their decision.

Difficulties with single-case studies

- As discussed above, the possibility that a patient had unusual brain architecture prior to brain damage raises the question of the legitimacy of trying to generalize from a single individual with brain damage to the nature of normal cognition. For example, the brains of split brain patients may have developed non-conventionally due to their epilepsy, and the patients may have created compensatory strategies that do not reflect normal cognition.

- Single-case studies cannot address theories that imply relationships between two variables (e.g. brain size and intelligence) since correlational designs need more than one subject.

- Sometimes the possibility that performance may vary over time is not taken into consideration – this is important since patients can vary from the acute to the chronic phase of brain damage. Therefore, if brain damage has been recent, it is important to study a single patient at a number of points in time in case their functioning is still stabilizing.

- Researchers may unwittingly fall into the trap of selecting a single patient because they appear to confirm a particular theory, while not seeking patients that might disconfirm the theory. As a result, it can sometimes be difficult to replicate findings from different laboratories.

Difficulties with group studies

- Grouping of subjects is legitimate in conventional experimental research since it assumes a certain degree of homogeneity within each group of participants. However, a group of neuropsychological patients is unlikely to show the same homogeneity in terms of brain damage – as discussed above, there is likely to be variability in the types and extent of lesions.

- Grouping subjects according to *syndromes* (a cluster of symptoms), such as Broca's or Wernicke's aphasia, will introduce variability since although the patients will share symptoms, there also tend to be many other behavioural differences (often overlooked).

- Subtle differences between subjects in their performance on a task can be masked when averaging data across groups.

- Why study groups of subjects when one compelling case study can be the exception that proves the rule? On the assumption that 'the architecture of cognition is constant across people' (Coltheart, 2001, p.18) (that is, the patient is *not* a 'Martian among us'), generalizing from the single case should be legitimate.

With such a diversity of issues, how should a neuropsychologist decide which methodology to choose? Perhaps the first consideration should be the resources available. Some research institutions (for example hospitals with a large focus on research) have access to large groups of patients whilst others can access only limited numbers. A second consideration is the particular field of research because patients with some types of deficit are extremely rare while other kinds of deficit occur more frequently. For example, Capgras Syndrome – in which a patient feels that his or her family have been replaced by impostors (e.g. Alexander *et al.*, 1979; see also **Pike and Brace, 2010**) – is so rare that it would be difficult to find two patients to study at the same time. Wernicke–Korsakoff syndrome, which is a cluster of deficits (the hallmark symptom being classical amnesia), is much more common and so group studies are possible (e.g. Albert *et al.*, 1979; Kopelman, 1989). Finally, the rigour with which researchers address methodological concerns is of relevance – if all the caveats of studying single cases are borne in mind, and a patient is tested thoroughly, then a single-case study can be highly informative.

6.6 Developmental versus acquired neuropsychological disorders

Brain damage can occur at any time in someone's life – it could happen pre-natally, in the womb, post-natally as a result of complications or due to a premature birth, during childhood accidents, or during adulthood. To further complicate matters, the cognitive system may have problems not due to brain damage but because of a genetically inherited disorder.

A developmental disorder is a condition that appears in childhood and is associated with a delay in the development of a psychological ability. Of course, the disorder may arise for different reasons, including a possible genetic basis. A disorder that arises because of physical brain damage is referred to as an 'acquired' one. So a child who had always had a reading problem, without experiencing brain damage, would be classified as having developmental dyslexia. Someone who could read but then has a reading impairment following a stroke would be classed as having acquired dyslexia. These two major groups themselves subdivide depending on the types of problems seen in patients. For example, in the field of acquired dyslexia, there exist a number of different forms such as 'surface dyslexia' (e.g. Marshall and Newcombe, 1973) and 'phonological dyslexia' (e.g. Beauvois and Dérousné, 1979).

For a number of reasons, more research has been carried out on acquired disorders than developmental ones. One reason is that with the former the assumption of subtractivity may be more legitimate – in inferring how the normal system works it may be more useful to look at one that used to work normally but has now been damaged, rather than one that never seemed to work normally. Since the reading system of a person with developmental dyslexia may not have formed normally, it may not be sound to draw conclusions about how the normal adult reading system works. However, the study of developmental disorders can still be extremely useful for understanding the problems that certain groups of young children and adolescents face in an attempt to find ways to help them. In recent years for example, dyslexia has been taken much more seriously in the school system, which now allows the children who suffer from it to gain the support they need. As knowledge grows about how to study such groups, this area will develop greatly.

Due to the issue of plasticity mentioned above, *when*, in an individual's life, they suffer from brain damage has important implications both theoretically and clinically. If damage occurs very early in life, then some level of neuronal repair and/ or a certain amount of reorganization may be possible. This is unlikely if damage occurs later in life. Hence, the same type of brain damage in childhood and adulthood can have very different consequences in terms of the permanent problems that remain with the patient.

For example, some babies who are born very prematurely, and whose lungs are not yet strong enough to circulate blood around the body sufficiently, suffer damage to the brain because it is starved of oxygen for a brief but crucial period of time. In one such baby, the only damage caused was in a very discrete but important part of the **hippocampus**, an area that is vital for memory (Vargha-Khadem *et al.*, 1997). Despite this, the baby grew up relatively normally and it was only at around the age of six that it was noticed that he had significant memory problems. Although he has quite severe problems with his memory, he is still able to hold down a job and look after himself to a certain degree. Adults who suffer the same brain damage to the hippocampus, however, have much greater difficulty in learning to cope because it is impossible for the brain to 'rewire' at that age and difficult to develop new coping strategies. For example, two very well-documented patients with severe amnesia – HM (Corkin, 2002) in North America and CW (Wilson and Wearing, 1995) in Britain – both have to live in care homes because of the impossibility of their living independent lives.

Summary

- Researchers need to be aware of the possibility that a patient may *not* be representative of the general population and that replication is therefore vital to support conclusions about normal cognition.
- Due to physical differences between any two brains and the fact that brain damage can often be diffuse rather than neatly localized, it is important to compare data from patients systematically both at the behavioural and neurological level.
- The assumption of subtractivity centres around the idea that what is observed in a patient is the effect of a whole cognitive system that has had certain modules impaired or removed whilst leaving the rest of the system intact. By applying this assumption systematically and with care, neuropsychologists aim to construct an understanding of the normal intact system.
- Researchers need to be aware of the possibility of plasticity both neurally (regrowth of brain tissue if damage occurs *very* early in life) and cognitively ('movement' or adaptation of a function) following brain trauma.
- Whether researchers should study single individuals or groups of patients is an important research question. There is no correct answer and there are many factors that determine the choice of method.
- It is necessary to distinguish between developmental disorders and those that are acquired following trauma. The application of methods and interpretation of results will depend on whether the behavioural problem is developmental or acquired.

7 Cognitive neuropsychological rehabilitation

As we have seen, cognitive neuropsychologists are trying to develop an understanding of normal intact cognition as well as a particular patient's deficits. Additionally, accurate assessment allows the clinician to see what problems a patient faces, and also what abilities are still preserved. As the understanding of the workings of the brain and cognition increase, so does the clinician's ability to devise techniques for helping and rehabilitating patients by capitalizing on the abilities that are known to be preserved and that can still allow some level of normal functioning.

Suppose a memory-impaired patient exhibits the pattern shown in Figure 3.17, i.e. a normally functioning STM and procedural memory with an impaired declarative memory.

Figure 3.17 Diagram of preserved and impaired abilities in amnesia – italics represents impaired forms of memory and bold represents intact forms

HM, for example, has been taught a mirror-drawing task in which he has to trace a line between two stars, one inside the other but he can only see the reflection of his hand in a mirror. It is possible to see if HM learns this by seeing how many errors (counted as the number of times he crosses the lines) he makes on successive trials (see Figure 3.18). Despite not being able to remember having done the task before, HM's error rate reduced greatly to the point of showing perfect performance (see Figure 3.19). A more practical example is provided by Hunkin *et al.* (1998) who showed how it was possible to teach a person with amnesia to use a computer for word processing (see Figure 3.20). This sort of skill can allow someone with memory impairment to have a degree of independence that would not have been possible previously.

Figure 3.18   HM's mirror-drawing task in which he can only see what his hand is drawing in the reflection of a mirror

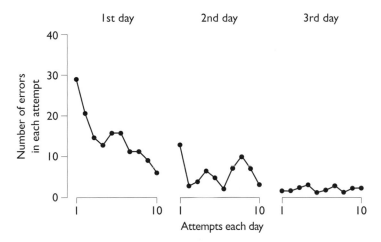

Figure 3.19   HM's mirror-drawing abilities improved with repeated attempts despite an impaired LTM since the number of his errors reduced over time

Figure 3.20 Hunkin *et al.* have demonstrated that it is possible to teach computer skills to a person with amnesia since completion times for the task reduce over time

With the knowledge that research studies like this have been successful in adding to the skill-base of a patient, neuropsychologists have been able to develop rehabilitation programs that do not require a normal LTM or conscious memory for previous learning. This is still a relatively new field in neuropsychology since researchers need to understand damaged and intact processes in patients before effective techniques can be devised. However, Wilson and colleagues (see, for example, Wilson *et al.*, 2001) have developed rehabilitation techniques, such as NeuroPage, a memory paging aid. Patients are taught the skill of checking the pager regularly over the course of a day, so that they can be reminded to do things that otherwise would be forgotten. See Box 3.3 for a remarkable case of a patient who has been taught to lead an independent life as a result of rehabilitation work.

3.3 — Research study

Rehabilitation of memory: the case of JC

Wilson *et al.* (1997) present the case of a patient (JC) who, while studying at university, suffered a brain haemorrhage that left him with damage to the left hemisphere. Whereas JC's STM was left intact, he had severe problems in transferring information to LTM. As a result, he was unable to continue with his studies. Over a period of time he was taught rehabilitation techniques that involved the use of external aids (such as writing things down in a notebook and keeping information on a databank wristwatch), mnemonics, rehearsal strategies and chaining (breaking a task into steps and learning them one step at a time). The remarkable result was that JC was able to go to technical college to learn a craft, furniture making, using his intact procedural memory. As JC said, 'When away from home, I used my coat as a base. I used my Dictaphone to plan my course work and found it was best to do the planning at the end of each session' (Wilson *et al.*, 1997, p.184). As a result of the success of this rehabilitation regime, JC was able to run a small business from home, buy a flat and even go on holiday on his own – all in a patient with a pure amnesia that prevents him from effectively transferring information from STM to LTM!

Wilson *et al.* suggest three predictors for the successful use of compensatory strategies:

1   The earlier the brain damage, the more chance there is of developing compensatory strategies.

2   Lack of other cognitive deficits.

3   A low score on the Rivermead Behavioural Memory Test (a test of everyday memory), a low score predicting a better ability to hold on to new information in a real-life setting.

It is fortunate that JC meets these criteria. Other patients may not do so, for example, if they were older when brain damage occurred or they have other difficulties such as language problems. However, the fact that cognitive neuropsychological research has helped devise ways of tapping the intact abilities of patients with brain damage in order to improve their standard of life shows how powerful neuropsychological methods can be. A continuing aim of neuropsychology is, by careful research, to understand as much as possible about the intact and damaged cognitive system to eventually help as many individuals as possible.

Summary

- As understanding of normal cognition and the effects of brain damage grow, clinicians are better placed to develop techniques for some aspects of rehabilitation.
- These techniques often involve capitalizing on the abilities that aren't compromised by brain damage (e.g. procedural and implicit memory in a memory-impaired patient).
- There are a number of predictors that are thought to determine the extent and success of rehabilitation and these include how early in life brain damage occurred and the lack or presence of deficits other than the central deficit.

8 Conclusion

This chapter has provided an overview of cognitive neuropsychology. A historical perspective is especially important since neuropsychology is a relatively new field that has shown substantial evolution. The goals of neuropsychology have developed from mere assessment of patients and understanding of what could be wrong with them (as in Broca's time) to the use of neuropsychology to reveal the nature of normal cognition. The goals evolved partly because of the availability of better techniques for assessing patients (e.g. standardized tests) and then better research paradigms that arrived as a consequence of the advent of cognitive psychology. Consonant with the development of goals, it has become clearer that there are numerous methodological issues that researchers need to take into consideration when studying patients and interpreting data. Finally, the chapter concluded with a description of one of the newest goals of neuropsychology – rehabilitation – which aims to apply some of the lessons learnt from studying damaged brains towards improving the lives of patients themselves.

Of course, neuropsychology is not a *stand-alone* method, nor does it pretend to be the 'best' one. It should be used in conjunction with other methods wherever appropriate. As a result, neuropsychology has informed many areas of cognition, such as: memory; the work on different forms of dyslexia (which has allowed sophisticated models of reading to be created); work on aphasia (which has allowed researchers and clinicians to understand the complexities of the production and comprehension of language); the work on problems faced by patients with object and face agnosia, also known as prosopagnosia (which has allowed an understanding of visual recognition processes). Through the continued application of neuropsychological techniques, in conjunction with other methods, our understanding of normal cognition will develop still further.

Now that you have read this chapter you can reinforce and extend your learning by reading an original journal article associated with it. The journal articles are available through the DD303 website. Remember these are original journal articles, so the style is different from that in this *Methods Companion* and don't be too concerned if you can't follow every detail.

Further reading

Andrewes, D.G. (2001) *Neuropsychology: From Theory to Practice*, Hove, Psychology Press. An excellent undergraduate level text book, with good coverage of all major areas of neuropsychology.

Ramachandran, V.S. and Blakeslee, S. (1998) *Phantoms in the Brain: Probing the Mysteries of the Human Mind*, New York, William Morrow. A book written specifically for the layperson. It provides a fascinating introduction to the investigation of brain damage with each chapter focusing on a patient with an intriguing neurological problem.

Rapp, B. (2001) *Handbook of Cognitive Neuropsychology*, Hove, Psychology Press. An advanced level book covering more complex issues within neuropsychology. It should not be read as an introduction.

References

Adolphs, R., Tranel, E., Damasio, H. and Damasio, A.R. (1994) 'Impaired recognition of emotion in facial expressions following bilateral damage to the human amygdale', *Nature*, vol.372, pp.669–72.

Aggleton, J.P. and Brown, M.W. (1999) 'Episodic memory, amnesia, and the hippocampal-anterior thalamic axis', *Behavioral and Brain Sciences*, vol.22, pp.425–89.

Albert, M.S., Butters, N. and Levin, J. (1979) 'Temporal gradients in retrograde amnesia of patients with alcoholic Korsakoff's disease', *Archives of Neurology (Chicago)*, vol.36, pp.546–9.

Alexander, M.P., Stuss, D.T. and Benson, D.F. (1979) 'Capgrass syndrome: a reduplicative phenomenon', *Neurology*, vol.29, pp.334–9.

Atkinson, R.C. and Shiffrin, R.M. (1968) 'Human memory: a proposed system and its control processes' in Spence, K.W. and Spence, J.T. (eds) *The Psychology of Learning and Motivation: Advances in Research and Theory*, pp.90–195, New York, Academic Press.

Baddeley, A.D. and Warrington, E.K. (1970) 'Amnesia and the distinction between long and short-term memory', *Journal of Verbal Learning and Verbal Behavior*, vol.9, pp.176–89.

Baddeley, A.D., Thomson, N. and Buchanan, M. (1975) 'Word length and the structure of short-term memory', *Journal of Verbal Learning and Verbal Behavior*, vol.14, pp.575–89.

Baddeley, A.D. and Hitch, G.J. (1977) 'Working memory' in Bower, G.A. (ed.) *Recent Advances in Learning and Motivation*, New York, Academic Press.

Bates, E. (1998) '"Recovery and development after trauma". Review of Broman, S. and Michel, M.E. "Traumatic head injury in children"', *Contemporary Psychology*, vol.43, pp.39–40.

Beauvois, M.F. and Dérousné, J. (1979) 'Phonological alexia: three discussions', *Journal of Neurology, Neurosurgery and Psychiatry*, vol.42, pp.1115–24.

Beschin, N., Basso, A. and Della Sala, S. (2000) 'Perceiving left and imagining right: dissociation in neglect', *Cortex*, vol.36, pp.401–14.

Bogen, J.E. and Vogel, P.J. (1965) 'Neurological status in the long term following cerebral commissurotomy' in Michel F. and Schott B. (eds) *Les Syndromes de Disconnexion Calleuse Chez L' Homme*, Lyon, Hospital Neurologique.

Broca, P. (1861/1965) 'Remarques sur le siège de la faculté du langage articulé suivies d'une observation d'aphémie' in Herrnstein, R. and Boring E.G. (eds) (1965) *A Source Book in the History of Psychology*, Cambridge, MA, Harvard University Press.

Bruce, V. and Young, A. (1986) 'Understanding face recognition', *British Journal of Psychology*, vol.77, pp.305–27.

Burton, M., Bruce, V. and Johnson, R. (1990) 'Understanding face recognition with an interactive activation model', *British Journal of Psychology*, vol.81, pp.361–80.

Butterworth, B. (1979) 'Hesitation and the production of verbal paraphasias and neologism in jargon aphasia', *Brain and Language*, vol.8, pp.133–61.

Caramazza, A. (1986) 'On drawing inferences about the structure of normal cognitive systems from the analysis of patterns of impaired performance: the case for single-patient studies', *Brain and Cognition,* vol.5, pp.41–66.

Cohen, N.J. and Squire, L.R. (1980) 'Preserved learning and retention of pattern analyzing skill in amnesia: dissociation of knowing how and knowing that', *Science*, vol.210, pp.207–10.

Coltheart, M. (1987) 'Reading, phonological recoding, and deep dyslexia' in Coltheart, M., Patterson, K.E. and Marshall, J.C. (eds) *Deep Dyslexia*, London, Routledge & Kegan Paul.

Coltheart, M. (2001) 'Assumptions and methods in cognitive neuropsychology' in Rapp, B. (ed.) *Handbook of Cognitive Neuropsychology*, Hove, Psychology Press.

Corkin, S. (2002) 'What's new with the amnesic patient H.M?' *Nature Reviews, Neuroscience*, vol.3, pp.153–60.

Craik, K. (1943) *The Nature of Explanation*, Cambridge, Cambridge University Press.

Damasio, A.R. (1994) *Descartes' Error: Emotion, Reason and the Human Brain*, New York, Grosset/Putnam.

Damasio, H., Grabowski, T., Frank, R., Galaburda, A.M. and Damasio, A.R. (1994) 'The return of Phineas Gage: clues about brain from skull of famous patient', *Science*, vol.264, pp.1102–5.

Damasio, H., Grabowski, T.J., Tranel, D., Hichwa, R.D. and Damasio, A.R. (1996) 'A neural basis for lexical retrieval', *Nature*, vol.380, pp.499–505.

Ellis, A.W. and Young, A.W. (1988) *Human Cognitive Neuropsychology*, Hove, London, Erlbaum.

Farah, M.J. and McClelland, J.L. (1991) 'A computational model of semantic memory impairment: modality specificity and emergent category specificity', *Journal of Experimental Psychology: General*, vol.120, pp.339–57.

Gaffan, D. and Heywood, C.A. (1993) 'A spurious category specific visual agnosia for living things in normal human and nonhuman primates', *Journal of Cognitive Neuroscience*, vol.5, pp.118–28.

Gall, F. and Spurzheim, G. (1970) 'Research on the nervous system in general and on that of the brain in particular' in Pribram, K. (ed.) *Brain and Behaviour: Vol. 1. Mood States and Mind*, Harmondsworth, Penguin Books.

Gazzaniga, M.S., Bogen, J.E. and Sperry, R.W. (1962) 'Some functional effects of sectioning the cerebral commisures in man', *Proceedings of the National Academy of Sciences USA*, vol.48, pp.1765–9.

Gazzaniga, M.S., Ivry, R.B. and Mangun, G.R. (1998) *Cognitive Neuroscience: The Biology of the Mind*, New York, London, W.W. Norton.

Glymour, C. (1994) 'On the methods of cognitive neuropsychology', *British Journal for the Philosophy of Science*, vol.45, pp.815–35.

Goodglass, H. and Kaplan, E. (1972) *The Assessment of Aphasia and Related Disorders*, Philadelphia, PA, Lea & Febiger.

Grant, D.A. and Berg, E.A. (1948) 'A behavioral analysis of degree reinforcement and ease of shifting to new responses in a Weigl-type card-sorting problem', *Journal of Experimental Psychology*, vol.38, pp.404–11.

Harlow, J. (1868) 'Recovery after severe injury to the head', *Publications of the Massachusetts Medical Society*, vol.2, pp.327–46.

Hillis, A.E. and Caramazza, A. (1991) 'Mechanisms for accessing lexical representations for output: evidence from a category-specific semantic deficit', *Brain and Language*, vol.40, pp.208–35.

Hitch, G.J. (2010) 'Working memory' in Kaye, H. (ed.) *Cognitive Psychology* (2nd edn), Milton Keynes, The Open University.

Humphreys, G.W. and Riddoch, M.J. (1987) *To See But Not to See: A Case Study of Visual Agnosia*, London, Erlbaum.

Humphreys, G.W., Riddoch, M.J. and Quinlan, P.T. (1988) 'Cognitive processes in picture identification', *Cognitive Neuropsychology*, vol.5, pp.67–104.

Hunkin, N.M., Squires, E.J., Aldrich, F.K. and Parkin, A.J. (1998) 'Errorless learning and the acquisition of word processing skills', *Neuropsychological Rehabilitation*, vol.8, pp.433–49.

Jansari, A., Davis, K. and Kapur, N. (2003) 'When long-term memory does not necessarily mean "forever": evidence of long-term amnesia (LTA) in a patient with temporal lobe epilepsy', *British Psychological Society (BPS) Cognitive Section Conference Abstracts*, Leicester, British Psychological Society.

Juola, P. and Plunkett, K. (1998) 'Why double dissociations don't mean much', *Proceedings of the 20th Annual Conference of the Cognitive Science Society, Vol.1–6*, Mahweh, NJ, Lawrence Erlbaum Associates.

Kopelman, M.D. (1989) 'Remote and autobiographical memory, temporal context memory and frontal atrophy in Korsakoff and Alzheimer patients', *Neuropsychologia*, vol.27, pp.437–60.

Le Voi, M. (2005) 'Connectionism', Reading 1 on DD303 website.

Lhermitte, F. and Beauvois, M.F. (1973) 'A visual–speech disconnection syndrome. Report of a case with optic aphasia, agnosic alexia and colour agnosia', *Brain*, vol.96, pp.695–714.

Lichteim, L. (1885) 'On aphasia', *Brain*, vol.7, pp.433–84.

Luck, S.J., Hillyard, S.A., Mangun, G.R. and Gazzaniga, M.S. (1994) 'Independent attentional scanning in the separated hemispheres of split-brain patients', *Journal of Cognitive Neuroscience*, vol.6, pp.84–91.

Marshall, J.C. and Newcombe, F. (1973) 'Patterns of paralexia: a psycholinguistic approach', *Journal of Psycholinguistic Research*, vol.2, pp.175–99.

McCarthy, R.A. and Warrington, E.K. (1990) *Cognitive Neuropsychology: A Clinical Introduction*, San Diego, CA, Academic Press.

Mulholland, P. and Watt, S. (2005) 'Symbolic modelling', Reading 2 on DD303 website.

Pike, G. and Brace, N. (2010) 'Recognition' in Kaye, H. (ed.) *Cognitive Psychology* (2nd edn), Milton Keynes, The Open University.

Pisella, L., Rode, G., Farne, A., Boisson, D. and Rossetti, Y. (2002) 'Dissociated long lasting improvements of straight-ahead pointing and line bisection tasks in two hemineglect patients', *Neuropsychologia*, vol.40, pp.327–34.

Ramachandran, V.S., Cronin-Golomb, A. and Myers, J.J. (1986) 'Perception of apparent motion by commissurotomy patients', *Nature*, vol.320, pp.358–9.

Rose, F.D. and Johnson, D.A. (1996) 'Brains, injuries and outcomes' in Rose, F.D. and Johnson, D.A. (eds) *Brain Injury and After*, Chichester, John Wiley and Sons.

Rutherford, A. (2010) 'Long-term memory: encoding to retrieval' in Kaye, H. (ed.) *Cognitive Psychology* (2nd edn), Milton Keynes, The Open University.

Sacchett, C. and Humphreys, G.W. (1992) 'Calling a squirrel a squirrel but a canoe a wigwam: a category-specific deficit for artefactual objects and body parts', *Cognitive Neuropsychology*, vol.9, pp.73–86.

Sacks, O. (1985) *The Man who Mistook his Wife for a Hat*, New York, Summit Books.

Scoville, W.B. and Milner, B. (1957) 'Loss of recent memory after bilateral hippocampal lesions', *Journal of Neurology, Neurosurgery and Psychiatry*, vol.20, pp.11–21.

Selnes, O.A. (2001) 'A historical overview of contributions from the study of deficits' in Rapp, B. (ed.) *The Handbook of Cognitive Neuropsychology*, Hove, Psychology Press.

Shallice, T. and Warrington, E.K. (1970) 'Independent functioning of the verbal memory stores: a neuropsychological study', *Quarterly Journal of Experimental Psychology*, vol.22, pp.261–73.

Sperry, R.W. and Gazzaniga, M.S. (1967) *Language Following Surgical Disconnection of the Hemispheres*, New York, Grune, Stratton.

Sutherland, N.S. (1989) *A Dictionary of Psychology*, London, Macmillan.

Tranel, E., Damasio, H. and Damasio, A.R. (1997) 'A neural basis for the retrieval of conceptual knowledge', *Neuropsychologia*, vol.35, pp.1319–27.

Vargha-Khadem, F., Gadian, D.C., Watkins, K.E., Connelly, A., Van Paesschen, W. and Mishkin, M. (1997) 'Differential effects of early hippocampal pathology on episodic and semantic memory', *Science*, vol.277, pp.376–80.

Warrington, E.K. and Shallice, T. (1984) 'Category specific semantic impairments', *Brain*, vol.107, pp.829–53.

Weiskrantz, L. (1986) *Blindsight: A Case Study and Implications*, Oxford, Clarendon Press.

Weiskrantz, L. (1987) 'Blindsight' in Boller, F. and Grafman, J. (eds) *Handbook of Neuropsychology*, vol.2, pp.375–85, Amsterdam, Elsevier Publishers.

Wernicke, K. (1874) 'Der aphasische Symptomenkomplex' (trans.) in *Boston Studies in Philosophy of Science*, vol.4, pp.34–97.

Wilson, B.A., J.C. and Hughes, E. (1997) 'Coping with amnesia: the natural history of a compensatory memory system' in Parkin, A.J. (ed.) *Case Studies in the Neuropsychology of Memory*, pp.179–90, Hove, Psychology Press.

Wilson, B.A., Ernslie, H.C., Quirk, K. and Evans, J.J. (2001) 'Reducing everyday memory and planning problems by means of a paging system: a randomised control crossover study', *Journal of Neurology, Neurosurgery and Psychiatry*, vol.70, pp.477–82.

Wilson, B.A. and Wearing, D. (1995) 'Amnesia in a musician' in Campbell, R. and Conway, M. (eds) *Broken Memories*, Oxford, Blackwell.

Young, A.W., Hay, D.C. and Ellis, A.W. (1985) 'The faces that launched a thousand slips: everyday difficulties and errors in recognizing people', *British Journal of Psychology*, vol.76, pp.495–523.

Young, A.W., Newcombe, F., de Hann, E.H.F., Small, M. and Hay, D.C. (1993) 'Face perception after brain injury', *Brain*, vol.116, pp.941–59.

Quantitative methods   Chapter 4

Martin Le Voi

1   Introduction

In this chapter you will learn about parametric univariate statistics, for which computer packages (such as SPSS, Statistical Package for Social Sciences) are available to take the grind out of the mathematics. You only need to understand what these statistics do, not all of the mathematics behind them. Univariate statistics are about tests with a single dependent variable.

This chapter assumes a previous understanding of probability and statistics corresponding to what you should have studied in a second-level course in psychology. It may help you to revise that work if you feel you are not entirely familiar with those concepts, although we do begin by covering some fundamentals. This chapter will assist you with understanding statistical concepts by presenting alternative and additional conceptualizations of these statistical ideas. Different students respond better to different ways of presenting statistical concepts, so it is hoped that presenting these ideas in various ways will help all students to understand them.

The chapter will specify exercises for you to carry out. Some are optional to help you understand points. Others should be considered to be the minimum you need to ensure you understand the concepts.

Starting with two fundamentals, the chapter moves on to consider the conceptual basis for analysis of variance, leading into a number of related topics.

2   Two fundamentals

2.1   Why do we do statistics?

Suppose I want to test the Stroop effect, in which people are expected to take longer to name the ink colour of a word if that word is the name of a different colour. I get one person and time him as he names the colour of 50 words which spell out non-colour words. I get another person and time her as she names the colour of 50 words, all of which are colour names which differ from the actual colour of the ink. The first participant takes 15 seconds, and the second takes 20 seconds. Have I proved my hypothesis? Do I even have evidence in support of it?

Well, I suppose the evidence is in support, but this evidence isn't much use because of the obvious problem that I have little idea what would happen if I tried it out on two new (different) people. The problem is that individual scores on the naming task will naturally vary, even if the colour words have no effect, because some people just do things faster than others. I want results which can be true of *general* human cognition, not just true of the particular participants I happened to pick on one day. In other words, I want to be able to generalize from the people who did my experiment to the general population of humans. How do I do this?

I could find another two people, and ask them to try the experiment. Trying it out on two more doesn't seem to be a specially satisfactory measure to ensure generalizability. So, I could try another 20 participants. Is this enough? How will I know if I can correctly generalize from my experiment to make statements about human cognition in general?

This is what statistics is all about. In the early twentieth century, scientists were casting around for arithmetically defined concepts which would permit this kind of generalization. Not just any mathematical idea would do. The essential feature of such an idea is that its value behaves in a systematic way when it is calculated from many samples from a population. In particular, it needs to have a defined **sampling distribution** (like that in Figure 4.3 in Section 3.2.1 of this chapter), so that we can see how its value varies from sample to sample in an expected way. We shall look at a demonstration of such systematic behaviour of a sampling distribution in Section 3.2.1.

Scientists came up with a number of concepts, called *statistics*, which have the required behaviour and allow us to draw conclusions (make *inferences*) about the population from the data in our sample. It is these **inferential statistics** that you will learn about here, so that you can find out how to make valid scientific judgements about theories and hypotheses from experimental data.

2.2   Estimating the mean: reducing error

One way of looking at statistical analysis is to consider it as an exercise in *prediction*. This will be particularly useful when we look at multiple regression later on. For now, consider the situation where I have measured the height of everyone in my country. If I was then asked to predict the height of one individual, who could be anyone at all from the population, what would be my best guess, my best *estimate*? You may well be thinking that the best estimate would be the average or **mean** height, and you would be right. But what is so special about the mean that makes it a good single estimate (in statistics we call it a **point estimate**)?

Table 4.1

Data values
6
2
1

Let's look at a smaller problem than the whole population of my country. Take the three numbers in Table 4.1. How do I decide what would be a good point estimate of these numbers? What we need to think of is *error*. The estimate I choose will, if applied to individuals, usually show some error, because it is, after all, an informed guess. So it's agreed, by definition, that the best estimate is the one which, when applied to *all* the individuals in my sample, ends up producing the **least error** when the total error is added up over all the numbers. Suppose I try the number 3 as an estimate for the numbers in Table 4.1. Guessing that number gives errors for all three numbers: 6 is higher by 3, 2 is lower by 1, 1 is lower by 2. We calculate the **total error** by adding up these numbers (ignoring whether they are higher or lower), so the total error for this estimate is 6 $(3 + 1 + 2)$. Is this the best estimate (i.e. the one with the lowest total error) that we can find? Try another number to see what happens to the error.

Spreadsheet exercise 1

For this and subsequent exercises, details of how to access the relevant files and software are given in the Introduction to this book.

You can try this very quickly by opening the spreadsheet exercise 1 file. It is in two different versions to be able to run on Microsoft Excel and Open Office spreadsheet applications (the latter is available as a download from the online Computing Guide).

Instructions

Open the spreadsheet EX1 (Excel).xlsx (Microsoft Excel) or EX1 (OO).ods (Open Office). You can see the three data points and a line representing the estimate. You move the estimate by typing a new value in the cell indicated by 'estimate: change this value'. As soon as you put a new value in and tell the spreadsheet to accept the value (often by pressing 'return'), the line representing the estimate will move and the value of the Total Absolute Error changes.

If you try this, you find there are better estimates than 3. Let's try 2. 6 is higher by 4, 2 is the same (0), while 1 is lower by 1. The total error is now only $(4 + 0 + 1) = 5$. So this is a better estimate. Actually, it can be proved that this is the best estimate for these three data points, and reduces the Total Absolute Error to the smallest value.

Table 4.2

Data values
8
5
2
1

Before we get excited that we've found a good definition of error and hence a good estimate, consider the numbers in Table 4.2. Measuring error as we have just specified, what is our best estimate? 3 might be good: the total error is $5 + 2 + 1 + 2 = 10$. How about 2? Here error is $6 + 3 + 0 + 1$, also 10. Let's try 4. Error is $4 + 1 + 2 + 3 = 10$ again. In fact there is no *unique* number between 2 and 5 (inclusive) which gives less error than any other number, so the estimate is no longer a point estimate, because any number between 2 and 5 is as good as any other.

Spreadsheet exercise 2

This is the same as spreadsheet exercise 1, but using the four data points in Table 4.2.

Instructions

Open the file EX2 (Excel).xlsx (Microsoft Excel) or EX2 (OO).ods (Open Office). You can change the estimate value by typing a new value in the cell marked 'estimate: change this value'. See how the Total Absolute Error changes for different values of the estimate.

The lack of a unique point estimate is rather undesirable. So mathematicians came up with another definition of error. (There were other reasons, too, which will come up as you learn more about statistics.) The new error measure involves *squaring* the error of each individual score before adding them up. (You square a number by multiplying it by itself.) So if we estimate 2 for the numbers in Table 4.1, the errors are:

6	$(6-2)^2 =$	$4^2 = 4 \times 4$	$=$	16
		+		
2	$(2-2)^2 =$	$0^2 = 0 \times 0$	$=$	0
		+		
1	$(1-2)^2 =$	$1^2 = 1 \times 1$	$=$	1
Total			$=$	17

This gives an error of 17. Is 2 the best estimate?

Spreadsheet exercise 3

Using spreadsheet exercise 3, can you find an estimate which gives a better (lower) total squared error? Again, there are two versions of the spreadsheet, EX2 (Excel).xlsx (Microsoft Excel) or EX2 (OO).ods (Open Office). Use the same procedures as in spreadsheet exercises 1 and 2.

Let's try the estimate 3. The errors are 3, 1 and 2, so total squared error is: $3^2 + 1^2 + 2^2 = 14$. So 3 is much better than 2 (or 4)! (Again, it can be proved that this is the best estimate for these numbers, although we do not burden you with that proof here.) Note that the best estimate depends on the choice we make about the error calculation. Using squared error gives a different best estimate from using absolute (non-squared) error. For the numbers in Table 4.2, 3 gives total squared error $5^2 + 2^2 + 1^2 + 2^2 = 34$. While for the estimate 4, the error is $4^2 + 1^2 + 2^2 + 3^2 = 30$. With 4, the error is reduced, and in fact 4 does give a *unique* point estimate which has less error than any other estimate. So the special property of this point estimate is that it gives the **least squared error** across all the scores being estimated.

Spreadsheet exercise 4

Use this spreadsheet exercise to explore values of the estimator to see the effect on squared error. The version for Microsoft Excel users is EX4 (Excel).xls, the version for Open Office users is EX4 (OO).ods.

What is this point estimate with least squared error? It is, in fact, the **mean** (or average). The mean is a point estimator of a population which has the special property of having the least squared error to all the scores being estimated. The concept of estimates having the least squared error is the *fundamental concept* behind an entire family of statistics called **parametric statistics**, which is the family of statistics you will learn about here.

To tidy up, what about the first estimate we considered in spreadsheet exercises 1 and 2? It had the special property that it was an estimate with the least 'non-squared' error (also known as the Least Absolute Deviation), and it is known as the **median**. The median, and statistics based on the Least Absolute Deviation, are fundamental to a family of statistics called **distribution-free** statistics, which you can learn about elsewhere, if you are curious. We will not cover them here.

Summary of Section 2

- Statistics are used to allow us to generalize our results beyond the participants in our sample.
- Parametric statistics are based on estimating parameters (such as the mean) which have the least squared error.
- Statistics based on Least Absolute Deviation, such as the median, make up a family of statistics called distribution-free statistics.
- Analysis of variance, multiple regression and analysis of covariance are all types of parametric statistics.

3   Analysis of variance

3.1   The conceptual basis for analysis of variance

This section provides an entirely intuitive description of analysis of variance (ANOVA), without using algebra, formulae, or even arithmetic. The intention is to ensure you have an intuitive grasp of what analysis of variance tries to do, so that you are not disturbed by the mathematical treatment frequently found in statistics books. We are assuming you know some basic concepts in statistics: four of them are covered in Box 4.1.

4.1

A revision of statistical inference

Key concepts: **null hypothesis**; **alpha (α) level**; **significance**; **Type I error**.

Statistical inference is a decision-making process based on the results of experiments. When your experiment has included a number of conditions, you need to decide (infer from the data) whether there is any difference between the conditions.

Your starting point is the **null hypothesis**. This states that there is no effect of conditions, so when it is true any difference between conditions must be because

---

you were unlucky in your sampling, and the results are due to random chance. It is important to remember that this can be a valid explanation of *any* set of results, no matter how large the difference between the conditions (we shall see in Section 3.2.1 that a big effect can occasionally be produced from a purely random sampling of conditions which were known not to differ).

By chance, some variations between conditions are more likely than others. Eventually, however, the difference between the conditions can be so unlikely that we allow ourselves the luxury of rejecting the null hypothesis. Usually, we say that when the chance of finding such a large difference between conditions in a sample, were the null hypothesis to be true, has fallen to one in 20 (5 per cent, or 0.05) or less, we believe that the difference is a real one, and *decide* (remember this is a decision-making procedure) to reject the null hypothesis. We then say that we have decided that the difference between our conditions results from a real (factual) difference, not one due to chance.

The chance level (or probability) at which we make that decision is the **alpha (α) level**. Another description of this is the *p value*. We have suggested its normal setting is 5 per cent: this is simply a *convention* that scientists adhere to (so is often referred to as 'a conventional level of **significance**'). If the alpha level has been exceeded (i.e. p value < 0.05), the result is known as a **significant** result.

Being ready to make this decision introduces a problem, however. The random nature of results has not gone away. With α set to 5 per cent, even when there really is no difference between conditions, 5 per cent of the time you will allow yourself to decide that there *is* a difference. This is a **Type I error**. It is a mistake (a Type I *error*) to decide your conditions are different when really they are not. But sometimes you are bound to make such mistakes if you allow yourself to decide there is a difference when the alpha level is exceeded. The intention of setting α to 1 in 20 (or 5 per cent) is to make such mistakes rare events, so that you (mostly) draw correct conclusions and don't get misled (often) by your errors.

3.2 What is analysis of variance?

Why do we do analysis of variance? Usually psychologists run experiments in which there are a number of different conditions, which they hope will affect the behaviour of experimental participants on a given dependent variable. The psychologist usually calculates the mean of the participants' performance within each condition, and what the experimenter wants to know is whether the difference between the means can be trusted. If the psychologist is interested in these differences between the means, then what is the justification for doing an analysis of the variance, which is apparently not focusing on the mean of the data? Indeed, what is the variance that is being analysed?

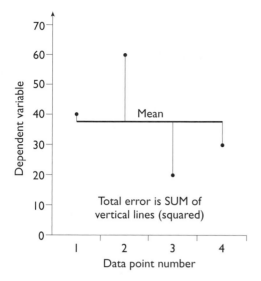

Figure 4.1

Look at Figure 4.1. Each datum – the singular form of the plural word 'data' – on this graph represents the response from one participant. Four participants were run. The experimenter has calculated the mean of these four participants on the dependent variable measured, and that mean is drawn horizontally across the figure. None of the data points in the figure lies exactly on this mean. Instead, they are all some distance away from it, shown in the figure by the line running from each data point to the mean. In general, data will be scattered around the mean like this, and that scatter can be measured by squared error, as described in Section 2.2. In parametric statistics, the measure of scatter used is called the **variance**, which is arrived at simply by taking the distance by which each datum varies from the mean and squaring it before adding all the squared differences together. This is known as the **sum of squares (SS)**, from which the variance is calculated by dividing by degrees of freedom (N − 1) (see Box 4.2).

4.2

Degrees of freedom (1)

As mentioned in Section 2.2, in parametric tests variance is measured by using the squared error of each datum. These are all added up to create a 'sum of squares' and divided by a number to arrive at an average error for each point (a 'mean square'). This is very like calculating the mean (when you add up all the numbers, and divide by the number of numbers you have), except that the total sum of squares is divided by a number called the **degrees of freedom**. If the total number of numbers is N, the degrees of freedom is *one less* than this number (N − 1). So:

$$\text{Variance or mean square} = \frac{\text{Total sum of squares}}{\text{N} - 1 \text{ (degrees of freedom)}}$$

The mean square is the usual definition of variance, in preference to the total sum of squares looked at in Section 2.

Why are the degrees of freedom one less than the total number of data points? The reason comes partly from the way the total sum of squares is calculated. The sum of squares is calculated by subtracting the mean from each data point before squaring it:

$$\text{Sum of squares} = \text{Sum (data point} - \text{mean)}^2$$

The problem is that the mean is itself calculated from the *same* data. When this happens you 'lose' a degree of freedom. Consider the case when you have three numbers 6, 8, and 10. The mean is 8. Suppose you are allowed to change any of these numbers, as long as the mean is kept constant at 8. How many numbers are free to vary? Perhaps counterintuitively, all three numbers cannot vary freely. If you change all three numbers haphazardly, most of the time the mean will no longer be 8. The point is that only two numbers can be *freely* changed if the mean is to stay the same. For example, if you change the 6 to a 7 and the 10 to a 13, the remaining number is *fixed* (not free): it must be a 4 to keep the mean as 8. The same argument applies for larger collections of numbers; with 50 numbers you can vary 49, the last number is always determined. So degrees of freedom are $N - 1$. Fortunately, statistics packages (such as SPSS) always calculate degrees of freedom correctly for you.

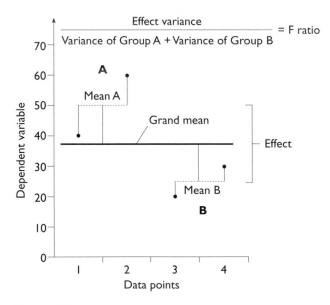

Figure 4.2

So what do we do when we analyse this variance? Look at Figure 4.2. In this figure, the same four data points from Figure 4.1 are plotted on the graph. The original mean of those data points, usually called the **grand mean**, is still plotted across the graph. However, there is now additional information available about the four data points. The data in fact belong to two groups, group A and group B. We can calculate means for each group, shown as mean A and mean B on Figure 4.2. Now, instead of measuring the distance of each datum from the grand mean, we can measure the distance by which each datum differs from its own group mean. These distances are shown on Figure 4.2. We can now add up this variability of the data points around the group means to give a new total variance.

However, you can see from Figure 4.2 that generally the distance each datum finds itself from the group mean is smaller than the distance each datum found itself from the grand mean. For data sets with many data points, it isn't necessarily the case that every datum will be nearer to its own group mean than it is to the grand mean. However, it is inevitable that as a whole the total distances of the data points from their own group means will be less than the total distances that the data are from the grand mean. In other words, this new variance that we have calculated (by measuring the distance from each datum to its own group mean) is less than the total variance calculated using the distance of each datum from the grand mean. Introducing the additional information that the data are divided into two groups, has resulted in a **reduction of variance** in the data. The results of many statistical tests, especially parametric ones, are frequently described in terms of the reduction in variance produced by the separation of the data into various groups etc. This is a very important concept in parametric statistics. The remaining variance of the data points around their group means (i.e. after separating the data points into the various groups) is called the **residual variance** (also referred to as **error variance**), and it is *always* less than the total variance.

So we have reduced the variance of the data points by measuring their distance from the group means instead of the grand mean. What has happened to the 'missing' variance? The missing variance has not disappeared. Instead of looking at the data points on Figure 4.2, look at the two group means. Each of the group means is itself some distance away from the grand mean. In other words, the group means themselves vary by some amount around the grand mean. Again, we can take the distance by which each group mean finds itself from the grand mean, and add up these squared distances to arrive at a total variance due to the dispersion of the group means around the grand mean. This variance is known as the **effect variance** or variance due to conditions. The arithmetic is carefully constructed so that the effect variance measured in this way is exactly the amount by which the total variance of the data points was reduced by measuring their distance from the group means rather than the grand means (this results from using squared distances and is another advantage of using squared error as the measure of dispersion).

Now, instead of having one value for the total variance of the data, we have two measures, or *sources*, of variance. One is the effect variance, and the other the residual variance. We have essentially **analysed the variance** by separating it, or **partitioning** it, into two sources. The final step is to perform a comparison to tell us whether the differences between the group means may have arisen by chance or not. Statisticians have worked out that a simple way to make this comparison is to compare the two variances we have just calculated by dividing one by the other. We divide the effect variance by the residual variance and the result is called a ratio – the **F ratio**, to be precise:

$$\frac{\text{Effect variance}}{\text{Residual variance}} \equiv \text{F ratio}$$

You can see from Figure 4.2 that as the two group means get further and further apart, the effect variance will get larger and larger. Similarly, if the data are found to cluster closer and closer to their own group means, then the residual variance gets smaller and smaller. *So the larger is the effect size compared to the dispersion of the data points around the group means, the bigger will be the F ratio.*

3.2.1   The F distribution

Now we've got an F ratio, what does it mean? We can see that as it gets bigger, the variance due to the conditions is large compared to the variance within the groups. Eventually, it will become large enough that we can decide to reject the null hypothesis (that there is no difference between the groups) and accept that our conditions had a real effect. How big does the F ratio need to be to make this decision?

When the F ratio was investigated in the first half of the last century, there were no computers. Also, the precise (mathematical) form of the distribution was unknown. Instead, the distribution had to be plotted by 'Monte Carlo' simulation. In this method, distributions are found by repeatedly using random procedures to sample, rather like throwing dice at casinos in Monte Carlo. I will show how this works with a demonstration. In this demonstration, I have three groups making up three conditions. I have created a population of 300 individuals, 100 in each of the groups. These three populations have different individual scores, but all three have the same mean; that is, the null hypothesis (of no difference) is *known* to be true of the population.

The Monte Carlo procedure works by taking a **random sample** of fifteen individuals, five from each group, and calculating the F ratio from that sample. This is then repeated with a new random sample a large number of times. I did it 10,000 times. Tables 4.3 and 4.4 show two of the samples.

Table 4.3   A sample of 15 participants in three groups

	Condition	
1	**2**	**3**
5.47	9.73	7.69
1.24	−2.43	19.93
5.82	9.23	9.28
27.92	27.38	16.57
2.19	−1.11	20.38

Table 4.4   A second sample of 15 participants in three groups

	Condition	
1	**2**	**3**
26.27	13.99	28.71
27.12	14.10	26.03
25.00	13.20	24.21
25.10	14.72	23.10
25.40	14.05	25.05

4.3

Degrees of freedom (2)

The F ratio has two degrees of freedom: one for the effect variance (numerator) and one for the residual variance (denominator). In our example with three conditions, there are 3 − 1 (N − 1), i.e. 2 degrees of freedom on the top (numerator) of the F ratio. Residual (or error) variance goes on the bottom. In our example of a Monte Carlo simulation, there are five individuals in each condition. Since we calculate the mean for *each* condition, we lose a degree of freedom each time, so there are four degrees of freedom among the five participants in *each* condition. Again, there are three conditions, so the total error degrees of freedom is 4 + 4 + 4 = 12. So the bottom (denominator) of the F ratio has 12 degrees of freedom.

The two degrees of freedom are conventionally written top first, then bottom. So the F ratio in our example would be written $F_{(2,12)}$.

You may notice that the degrees of freedom here add up to 14 (12 + 2), which is one less (N − 1) than the total number of participants (15). So it all adds up nicely.

These two samples in Tables 4.3 and 4.4 respectively produce two different F ratios, one quite small ($F_{(2,12)} = 0.647$) and one very large ($F_{(2,12)} = 117$) (see Box 4.3 for an explanation of the subscripted degrees of freedom for these ratios). We have 10,000 of these F ratios, varying in size (and remember, all these samples came from a population in which the null hypothesis is known to be true). So we can plot a distribution of these values of F.

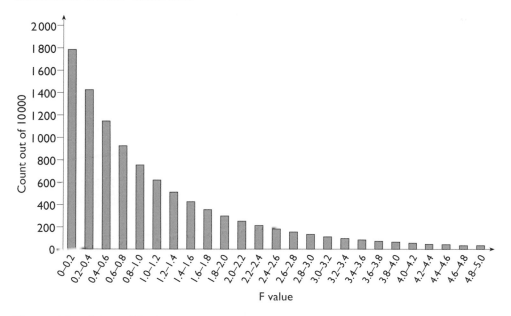

Figure 4.3   Count of F values

Figure 4.3 shows the distribution of these F values by counting how many F values in the 10,000 samples fall into each range. So, for example, 1,785 F values fell in the range 0 to 0.2, while only 30 fell in the range 4.8 to 5. The best way to use this distribution is to plot a **cumulative distribution**. A cumulative distribution counts all the values of F which are less than a certain value. So, for example, I found that the number of F values between 0 and 0.2 is 1,785, and in this sample 1,424 F values lie between 0.2 and 0.4. So the cumulative number of F values up to 0.4 is 3,209. The counts are also converted to a **probability**, by dividing the count (e.g. 3,209) by the total number of samples (10,000): so the cumulative probability is 0.3209. We can plot these cumulative values on a graph.

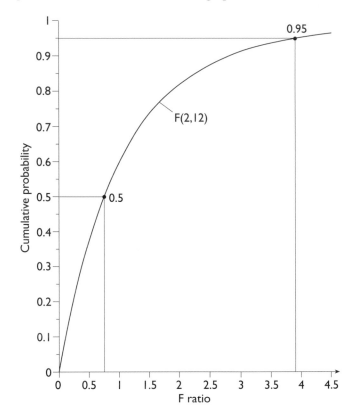

Figure 4.4 Cumulative F distribution

Figure 4.4 shows the cumulative probability of the F values in my sample of 10,000. Plotting the distribution in this way makes it easy to find values for F which correspond to the lower part of the distribution. For example, 50 per cent of the F values fall below the number 0.74. A much more useful cut-off is the 95 per cent point. Here we see that the F value at the 95 per cent point is 3.89.

You should remember that we reject the null hypothesis if the statistic we calculate has a less than 5 per cent (0.05) chance of being as big as it is when the null hypothesis is known to be true (see Box 4.1 at the start of Section 3.1). So if the cumulative probability between 0 and 3.89 is 95 per cent, there is only a 5 per cent chance of getting an F ratio larger than 3.89. This therefore is the **critical value** above which, in an experiment, we would reject the null hypothesis and accept that our conditions differ.

This critical value is only true for the particular F distribution we have looked at. This is because the F distribution changes with the number of groups and the number of participants in each group. This is expressed in the degrees of freedom for the F ratio. Figure 4.5 plots two cumulative F distributions, one with (2,12) degrees of freedom, one with (1,4) degrees of freedom. You can see the distributions are different, and they cut the critical 95 per cent value at different points (critical values at 95 per cent are $F_{(2,12)} = 3.89$, $F_{(1,4)} = 7.71$).

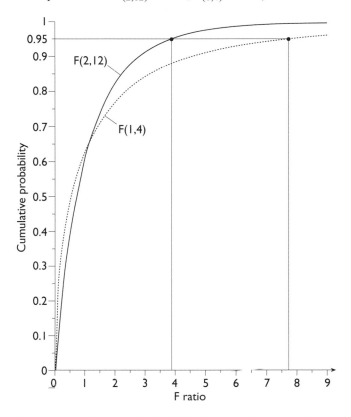

Figure 4.5 Two cumulative F distributions: $F_{(2,12)}$ and $F_{(1,4)}$

In the last century, these critical values were placed in large tables so that scientists could look them up to see if the value of F from their experiment fell above (in the 5 per cent region) or below (in the 95 per cent region) the critical value for their experiment. Nowadays, we have equations for the F distributions and computers calculate the exact point on the cumulative F distribution on which a particular value falls. For example, my spreadsheet package has an FDIST function, and if I give this function the $F_{(2,8)} = 8.9$ value, it tells me it falls at the 0.00924 level, so it is easily in the 5 per cent rejection region (this function is used in the spreadsheet exercises). In fact the function prints the p value 0.00924 showing how unlikely it is to have occurred by chance. Statistical analysis packages such as SPSS also automatically print this probability.[*]

---

[*] I must confess here that the graphs in Figures 4.3 and 4.4 used the spreadsheet function, not a Monte Carlo method. The Monte Carlo simulation for repeated measures (Section 5.1) is genuine, however.

SPSS exercise 1: One-way between-subjects ANOVA

Analyse the data file 1-WayBetween-SubjectsAnova.sav. You may wish to consult a book to guide you through the analysis in SPSS, or you can find a guide at The Open University's OpenLearn website (http://openlearn/) and on the DD303 website.

The psychologist, therefore, is able to analyse the variance of his or her data into two sources (effect variance, and residual (or error) variance), and, by comparing them, discover whether the reduction in variance of the data produced by separating them into several groups can be considered to be due to chance or not.

3.3   Analysis of variance with more than two conditions

The example discussed above had only two conditions. However, the discussion can be directly extended to the case where there are more than two treatments. Let us consider a simple one-way analysis of variance. The data in Table 4.5 have been taken from eight participants in an experiment. The eight participants are divided into four groups, producing two participants in each group. Two participants may not seem very much to give a result for each group. However, any number of participants greater than one is sufficient to give a calculation of the variance. You can see the data plotted out in Figure 4.6.

Table 4.5

Group	A		B		C		D	
	Participant	Data	Participant	Data	Participant	Data	Participant	Data
	1	35	3	65	5	25	7	25
	2	45	4	55	6	15	8	35
Group mean	40		60		20		30	

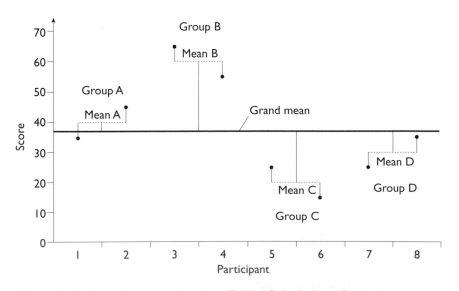

Figure 4.6   The eight data points from Table 4.5 divided into four groups

Given the information that these eight data points are divided into four groups, A, B, C and D, we can analyse the variance in exactly the same way as we did in Section 3.2. The group mean for each of the four groups is calculated, and the distance of each datum from its own group mean is measured. Once again, putting each datum into a group results in the residual variance of the data points about their own group means being less than the total variance. There has been a reduction in the variance of the data. The missing variance has not gone away. Again, each of the group means can be said to vary about the grand mean, and the amount by which each group mean differs from the grand mean can be measured. This distance is shown for each group mean in Figure 4.6. The effect variance is calculated by adding up all of these squared distances from each of the group means (and dividing by degrees of freedom). Again, the analysis of variance proceeds by comparing the effect variance against the residual variance to see if the effect variance is so much larger that the discrepancy cannot be attributed to chance. Having calculated the F ratio it is an easy matter to look in the appropriate part of the statistical tables to see the probability that it arose by chance.

In this example, an analysis of variance produces an F ratio (with three and four degrees of freedom – see Box 4.3) of 11.67. What does this F ratio mean?

If you look in a table of F ratios, the chance of getting an $F_{(3,4)}$ ratio as high as 11.67 when there is no difference between the means (the null hypothesis is true) is less than 0.05. In these circumstances, we usually decide to reject the null hypothesis, and conclude that there actually is a real difference between the means which is not due to chance variation. So, in the scientific context of the experiment that we discussed in this section, we consider that there are some real measurable differences between the four groups used in this experiment. In other words, the null hypothesis, that there are no differences between any of the conditions, is false.

In this example, there are four treatment groups being compared. However, any number of treatment groups greater than one can be used in the analysis of variance.

Spreadsheet exercise 5

Spreadsheet exercise 5 contains the data for this analysis of variance: EX5 (Excel).xlsx (Microsoft Excel) or EX5 (OO).ods (Open Office). You may find it useful to try changing the data to see what happens and give you a 'feel' for analysis of variance (ANOVA).

Instructions

In this spreadsheet, you can see a table containing the participants' scores. You can change the data for any participant by selecting that cell and typing in a new value.

1   Choose the point with the highest value in the first group. Enter a smaller value (e.g. 40). Make sure the value has been accepted by pressing return. You will see the grand mean change on graphs 1 and 3, and the mean of group A change on graphs 2 and 3. You will also see new values for the sum of squares appear. The total sum of squares will have gone up, because you moved the point away from the grand mean. The error (residual) sum of squares will also go up, because you moved the point away from its group mean. Because of this, the F ratio will have gone down. As the F ratio

reduces, the p value goes up. If you moved the point far enough, the p value will have gone higher than 0.05, making the result non-significant.

2   In each group, select the smaller value and enter a number which is nearer in value to the data point for the other participant in the same group. Watch what happens to the error (residual) sum of squares as you do this. The closer the points in each group get together, the smaller the error sum of squares becomes. This is because you are reducing the disagreement (error) between the data in each group and their own group mean. As the squared error falls, the F ratio rises. This can rise indefinitely. However, you will notice η^2 (eta-squared) does not rise higher than 1 (more on this in Section 6.3). So the more the data cluster tightly around the group means and therefore agree on the effect of conditions, the higher the F ratio and the more likely it is that we will get a significant result.

Summary of Section 3

- Analysing variance means partitioning the total variance of a series of data points into different sources of variance, such as the effect variance and the residual variance.
- The information introduced into the analysis by dividing the data into the appropriate groups (conditions) is evaluated by comparing the effect variance with the residual variance.
- If the reduction in the variance of the data points produced by grouping them in conditions is large, the F ratio calculated by dividing the effect variance by the residual variance may be larger than expected by chance alone, and we would feel justified in concluding that the division of the data points into those groups had a meaningful basis.

4   Multiple factor analysis of variance

The main conceptualization above, namely the partitioning of total variance in order to arrive at values for different sources of variance, is the fundamental concept in the analysis of variance. We now go on to consider how these concepts are extended into multi-factor or multiple factor analysis of variance.

If you look back at Figure 4.6, you will recall that in that analysis of variance there were eight individual data points which we then considered to be grouped into four different groups. An analysis of variance performed in that way would have found whether locating the data in the four different groups resulted in a significant reduction in the residual variance. One of the sources of variance identified, therefore, was the amount by which the four group means vary from the grand mean. That was known as the effect variance.

However, there is an analogy between Figure 4.6 and Figure 4.1. In Figure 4.6, the means of the four different groups vary about the grand mean. In Figure 4.1, four individual participants were varying around the grand mean. From Figure 4.1 to Figure 4.2 we discovered what happened if we partitioned the variance of the four participants into the effect variance resulting from knowing that two of the participants belonged to one group and two of the participants to another group. This left the residual variance and an effect variance due to the grouping. Exactly the same operation can be achieved with the group means in Figure 4.6. Suppose I give you the additional information that groups A and B are in fact data from only men and groups C and D are data from only women. Therefore, we could consider groups A and B together and groups C and D together (see Figure 4.7).

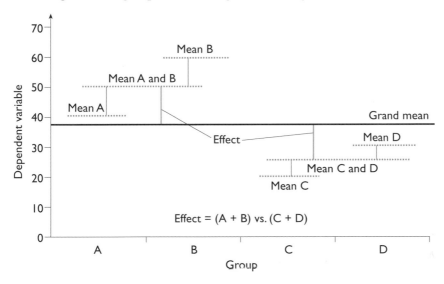

Figure 4.7   Main effect from men (A and B) versus women (C and D)

In Figure 4.7 we are ignoring the data from the participants for the moment, and have simply plotted the four group means. The two groups A and B taken together have a mean overall. This could be described as the mean for the men. Similarly groups C and D themselves have a common mean which could be called the mean for the women. These two overall means differ from the grand mean. The amount by which these means differ from the grand mean is the effect variance of the comparison between the men and the women. We have performed precisely the same operation as that between Figure 4.1 and Figure 4.2. Between Figure 4.6 and Figure 4.7, the treatment variance has been partitioned into an overall effect variance, men compared to women, leaving some residual variance.

In a multi-factor experiment, separating the group means into just two conditions is often not the only way of partitioning the variance. In this case, suppose I told you that groups A and C consisted only of left-handed participants whereas groups B and D comprised only right-handed participants. We could then calculate the overall mean for groups A and C taken together and the overall means for groups B and D taken together (see Figure 4.8).

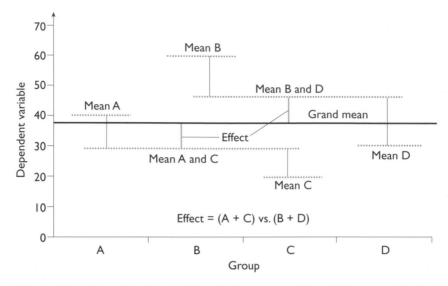

Figure 4.8 Main effect from left-handed participants (A and C) versus right-handers (B and D)

Once again, the means for groups A and C and the means for groups B and D differ from the grand mean. Again, this comprises a source of variance which we have partitioned from the overall variance of the treatment effects.

This is an example of a multi-factor experiment. There are two **factors**, the sex of the participant and the handedness of the participant. Each factor has a number of **levels**; in this case, sex has two levels (male and female), and handedness has two levels (right- and left-handed). These two factors, each with two levels, form four groups (the four groups are male left-handers, male right-handers, female left-handers and female right-handers). A simple 'one-way' analysis of variance simply partitions the variance into the effect variance due to these four groups and the residual variance of the participants. A multi-factor analysis of variance involves partitioning the variance of the four treatments into the two factors; that is, the male versus the female groups, and the left-handed versus the right-handed groups. In addition to these **main effects** the two factors combine in an **interaction**.

4.1 Interactions

What is an interaction? We saw with Figures 4.6, 4.7 and 4.8 that four groups of subjects A, B, C and D could in fact be meaningfully grouped into two factors, sex and handedness. These two factors allowed a way of grouping the four means in two different ways. First, A was grouped with B and compared with the remaining two groups. Second, A was grouped with C and compared with the other two groups together. This leaves a third grouping where group A is grouped with D and compared with the other two together (group B with group C). This is the interaction comparison. What does it mean?

The main factors, sex and handedness, were easy to understand, since sex effectively compared men against women, and handedness compared left handers against right handers. In the interaction grouping, however, male right-handers are paired with female left-handers and compared against the group of male-left handers with female right-handers. You can see from this pairing that different levels of each factor are paired with their opposite. The factors are said to be **crossed** with each other. What is this interaction term testing? Let's look more closely at the pattern of data.

Suppose the four group means were those shown in Figure 4.9. You can see that the value for left-handers is always above the value for right-handers and the values for men are always above the values for women. So the main factors produce a difference between their group means. To emphasize, there is a measured *difference* between the scores for left-handers and the scores for right-handers. Similarly, there is a measured difference between the scores for men compared with the scores for women. Look at Table 4.6.

Table 4.6 Table showing the overall differences due to the main effects (handedness and gender)

	Men	Women	Both sexes taken together
Left-handers	60	40	50
Right-handers	50	30	40
Left- and right-handedness taken together	55	35	

Overall difference for left-handers vs. right handers: 50 − 40 = 10

Overall difference for men vs. women: 55 − 35 = 20

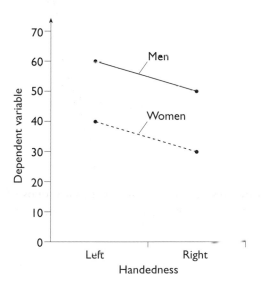

Figure 4.9 Data from Table 4.6

The main effects in the multi-factor analysis of variance evaluate these overall differences: is the difference of 10 between left-handers and right-handers more than you would expect by chance? Is the difference of 20 between men and women more than would be expected by chance?

The interaction takes this analysis a stage further. It looks at the differences found in the sub-cells of the table (see Table 4.7).

Table 4.7 Table showing the differences due to handedness within the two sexes

	Men	**Women**
Differences between handedness scores	10 (60 – 50)	10 (40 – 30)

Difference of the differences scores: 10 – 10 = 0

It then asks, are these two differences between handedness scores *different from each other*. So is the difference between male left-handers and male right-handers (10) different from the difference between female left-handers and female right-handers (10)? In this case, the two differences are identical, so there is no 'difference of the differences': there is no interaction.

Previously, we noted that the interaction combines A + D (left-handed men + right-handed women), and compares with B + C (right-handed men + left-handed women). You can see from Table 4.6 that A + D = 90, and B + C = 90: the same result of 'no difference'.

Suppose the data were as in Table 4.8 (plotted in Figure 4.10).

Table 4.8 New (fictitious) data for the interaction test

	Men	**Women**
Left-handers	60	40
Right-handers	40	50

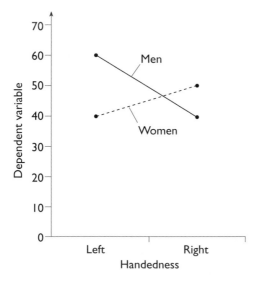

Figure 4.10 Data from Table 4.8

What is the 'difference of the differences' now? For men, left-handers score greater than right-handers by +20. However, for women, left-handers score 10 less than right-handers, so the difference is –10. These two differences, +20 and –10, are not identical so there may well be a 'difference of the differences' (i.e. an interaction is found). Again, comparing A + D (110) with B + C (80), the same difference of 30 is found.

An interaction means that the effect of handedness for men is somehow different from the effect for women. In this case, there is a clear difference, since male left-handers have higher scores, while female right-handers have the higher scores. Therefore, in this (fictional) example, *understanding the effect of handedness can only be understood if the context of gender is considered because there is an interaction.*

The idea of 'difference of differences' is most easily seen in the graphs of results. When the 'difference of differences' is zero, the lines will be parallel, as in Figure 4.9. But when the interaction is significant the lines are not parallel, since the differences change. This is true also when the experiment has more than two levels in one of the factors. Figure 4.11 illustrates several sets of results with lines not parallel (showing different interaction patterns).

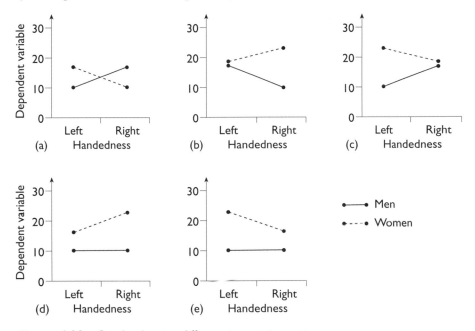

Figure 4.11   Graphs showing different interaction patterns

SPSS exercise 2

Analyse the data file 2-WayBetween-SubjectsAnova.sav. You may wish to consult a book to guide you through the analysis in SPSS, or you can find a guide at The Open University's OpenLearn website (http://openlearn/) and on the DD303 website.

4.2 Degrees of freedom

With the four groups of participants we were talking about above in relation to gender and handedness, we looked at all three possible pairings that group A can join and be tested against the remaining two groups (A with B, A with C, and A with D). There are no more possible pairings because we have used up all the three degrees of freedom available in the set of four data points (see Box 4.3).

Summary of Section 4

- The concept of partitioning variance (see Section 3.2) extends to creating partitions based on independent factors, of which there may be more than one.
- Each factor has an effect variance component unique to itself, which can be tested for significance by an appropriate F ratio.
- When more than one factor is involved, the effect of that factor may depend on the context of the other factors. If it does, then an interaction between the factors has been found.
- Interactions are made visible by looking at graphs of main effects. Lines connecting levels in one factor are found not to be parallel across levels of the other factor when an interaction is present.

5 The assumptions underlying analysis of variance and most parametric statistics

You should now understand the underlying logic of analysis of variance, which results in the generation of an F ratio to test whether conditions have an effect which cannot be ascribed to chance. Calculating the F ratio is a numerical procedure, and the F ratio is defined simply as the ratio of two variances. I commented in Section 3.3 above that, having calculated the F ratio, we use tables calculated by statisticians to see whether the value of this statistic allows us to reject the interpretation that the results were due to chance. We now have to look closely at what statisticians had to do to create those tables. This is because the creation of those tables is only possible if certain restrictive assumptions about the data are made. Those assumptions are as follows:

1   The data points are distributed around means according to the normal distribution (the normality assumption).

2   The variance of the data points within each of the groups (such as the four groups A, B, C and D in Figure 4.6) is the same (the homogeneity of variance assumption).

3   The observations are independent: knowing the value of one observation should tell us nothing about the value of another observation (the independence assumption).

These assumptions are very important. This chapter assumes you are familiar with what a normal distribution is, and under what conditions it may be found.

If the data which are being analysed are not normally distributed, then the tables of the F statistic found in statistics books are inaccurate. If those tables are inaccurate, then the scientific judgements being based on the analytical results are suspect. In other words, scientists doing analysis of variance with data that are not from a normal distribution are liable to make mistakes by drawing the wrong conclusions.

In general, most modern psychologists make few corrections for violating assumptions. This is because the F test is 'robust' to some violations: that is, our decisions remain reasonably reliable even when assumptions do not hold. However, you should be aware of these assumptions and ready to act if necessary. When it comes to repeated measures ANOVA, however, violation of one of the assumptions is routinely handled in the analysis.

5.1   Repeated measures

So far, we have discussed experiments when each participant serves in one experimental condition. These are between-participants designs. These are excellent research designs. However, some consider that these designs may be weakened by large individual differences between participants. These individual differences create some of the residual error which the experiment must overcome in order to detect a difference between the treatments.

Table 4.9   Three participants with repeated measures

		Conditions			Participant mean
		1	2	3	
	1	40	37	39	38.6
Participants	2	20	16	18	18
	3	10	4	7	7
Condition mean		23.3	19	21.3	

In another experimental design, the participants do all of the conditions in one or more factor(s), meaning that empirical measurements are repeated on each participant; this is known as a **repeated measures** design. Three participants in a repeated measures design are shown in Table 6.9. You can see that there are large individual differences between the participants, and (in this case) smaller differences between the treatments. In the analysis of variance, it is the three differences between the treatments (1 vs. 2, 1 vs. 3 and 2 vs. 3) for *each* individual which are used to measure the error variance. The idea is that this bypasses the individual differences and eliminates them (at least in part) from the error term.

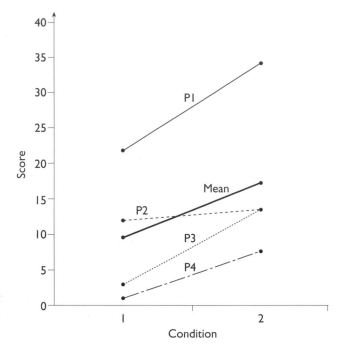

Figure 4.12   Repeated measures analysis

Figure 4.12 is another illustration of repeated measures analysis. Four participants have been measured in two conditions. The data for each participant have been joined together with a line. The figure also shows the mean for the two conditions, also joined by a line. You can see that the data for participant 1 (P1) are much higher overall than the others. But this *overall* difference between participants does not matter for the analysis. What matters is the lines joining the two conditions. If these lines mostly agree that one condition is better than the other, then the repeated measures analysis will allow us to conclude that the two means do differ. Here, the four participants all have lines which slope upwards (left to right), and additionally these slopes are in reasonable agreement, so that the statistical analysis ($F_{(1,3)}$ = 12.86) is significant (see spreadsheet exercise 6).

Spreadsheet exercise 6

Spreadsheet exercise 6 uses the data which created Figure 4.12. You can use this to explore how repeated measures analysis is sensitive to agreement between the participants. Example exercises follow.

Instructions

Open the spreadsheet EX6 (Excel).xlsx (Microsoft Excel) or EX6 (OO).ods (Open Office).

Exercise 6.1

Select the biggest number. Type in a new (lower) value. The analysis of variance table updates, and you should see that the mean square (MS) for the condition has reduced, while the MS for the error term has increased. As a result the F ratio, on which the statistical test depends, has reduced a lot, and the probability level (Prob) is not significant.

What has happened is that there is now quite a lot of disagreement between the participants about whether condition 2 is better than condition 1, since three participants have condition 2 better than condition 1, unlike the fourth participant. With so much disagreement between the participants, the result is not significant.

Exercise 6.2

In this exercise, which is a bit fiddly, try to move the data points for three participants so they are all parallel to the fourth. You can do this by moving one datum for each participant. Select the smallest ones. Type in a new (higher) value, and 'play' with the values until the lines become more parallel.

As you make the slopes all more parallel, you are increasing the agreement between the participants. The more you do this, the MS error term will get smaller and smaller. Meanwhile the F ratio will get larger, so the result is more significant. Indeed, if all four lines are *exactly* parallel, the MS error term will be zero! What happens to the F ratio then?

You can try other patterns of agreement between the lines to see the effect on the F ratio. For example, you could try moving *both* data points for one participant (e.g. participant 1) the same amount in the same direction. If you do this accurately, so that the slope does not change, the MS values for condition and error should not change, leaving the result as it was before.

What does change? The mean square (MS) value for the between-subjects term changes. A statistical test is not usually performed on this source of variance.

Note that the degrees of freedom change in repeated measures. Suppose I decide to measure three treatments five times each. In the between-subjects design, I need fifteen participants, five in each group, and my F ratio will have 12 degrees of freedom (four from each group) in the denominator. However, in the repeated-measures design, I will use five participants repeatedly to give the fifteen measures. Because it is the differences between the treatments which is analysed, or (equivalently) because we discard the individual differences between the five participants (and hence lose four, $N-1$, degrees of freedom), we only have 8 degrees of freedom in the denominator. This means we have to have a higher F ratio in the repeated measures design to reach significance. The 5 per cent critical value for the between-groups design $F_{(2,12)}$ is 3.89, while the 5 per cent critical value of the repeated measures design $F_{(2,8)}$ is 4.46. The F ratio needs to be 15 per cent higher in the second case. Of course, we may decide to run more participants in the repeated measures design, which would increase the degrees of freedom.

A real problem is the fact that one of the assumptions behind analysis of variance has been violated. This is the independence assumption. Because we measure the same participant repeatedly, the data are no longer independent. Consider the example in Table 4.9. You can see that knowing the score from one condition for one participant gives us a good guess about the values of scores on the other two treatments for the same participant. The result is that the scores on the three conditions are **correlated** with each other: a clear violation of independence.

Fortunately, statisticians have used a mathematical analysis to show that the independence assumption can be replaced with an assumption called **sphericity**. The sphericity assumption is made about the correlations between the conditions. In

Table 4.9, there are three correlations, between Condition 1 and Condition 2, Condition 1 and Condition 3, Condition 2 and Condition 3. *The sphericity assumption is that these correlations are the same*. If they are the same, we can use the F distribution appropriate for the normal degrees of freedom (such as F(2,8) in the example above). But what if they are not?

5.1.1   Approximating the F distribution

Let's take a look at a situation where these correlations are different. I've created a dataset based on a population of 100 participants, with repeated measurements across three conditions. In this data set, the correlations between the conditions are very different (see Table 4.10).

Table 4.10   Correlations between conditions in a population of measurements

Condition pairs	Correlation
Condition 1 with Condition 2	0.7
Condition 1 with Condition 3	0.1
Condition 2 with Condition 3	−0.6

As before, the *means* of the three conditions are exactly the same, so the null hypothesis is *known* to be true. After sampling five participants from this population 10,000 times, and calculating the F ratio for each sample, we can plot the cumulative F distribution.

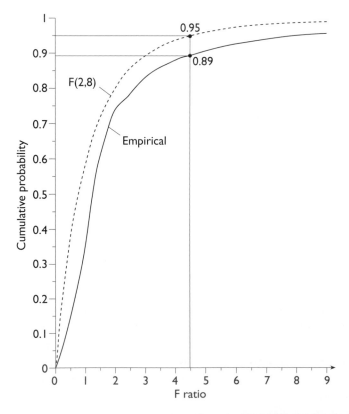

Figure 4.13   Empirical and exact $F_{(2,8)}$ cumulative F distributions

Figure 4.13 plots our empirical $F_{(2,8)}$ distribution against the theoretical $F_{(2,8)}$ distribution which would apply if the sphericity assumption held. You can see the empirical distribution is everywhere systematically lower than the ideal $F_{(2,8)}$ distribution. If we were to use the ideal $F_{(2,8)}$ distribution, we would make many more Type I errors than we would expect. This is because the 5 per cent $F_{(2,8)}$ critical value we would normally use is 4.46. Looking at the empirical distribution, we find that this value gives an actual Type I error rate of 11 per cent. This represents the 0.89 point on the cumulative distribution. We are quite a long way out. Therefore, our Type I error rate has risen from 5 per cent to 11 per cent, and we would only know this by doing a Monte Carlo test: not something to be done routinely. So we can't use the usual critical value found in our F tables. What can we do?

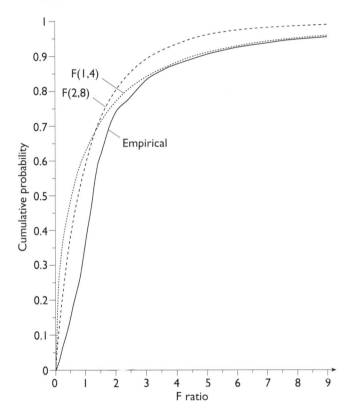

Figure 4.14   One empirical and two theoretical F distributions

We need to try to approximate the empirical F distribution. Figure 4.14 has another cumulative F distribution added: $F_{(1,4)}$. You can see, in comparison with the $F_{(2,8)}$ distribution, that it lies above it at the left-hand (lower) end, and below it at the right-hand (upper) end. Compared with the empirical F distribution, it doesn't look like a good approximation. It is quite a long way away at the lower end. But that doesn't really matter, it is the top end that matters. Around the 95 per cent area, the $F_{(1,4)}$ distribution is very close to the empirical distribution. The 5 per cent $F_{(1,4)}$ critical value is 7.7, which is at the 6 per cent point on the empirical distribution. This is obviously a big improvement.

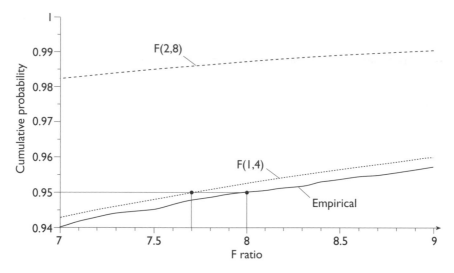

Figure 4.15 Three cumulative F distributions at the 95 per cent point

You can see from Figure 4.15 how close the $F_{(1,4)}$ distribution is as an approximation to the empirical distribution over the important area around the 95 per cent level.

So the trick to approximating the empirical distribution is to choose another F distribution which is close to it. A mathematical analysis shows this can be done by calculating a correction factor, epsilon (ε), from the correlations between the treatments. There are two ways of calculating epsilon, one due to Greenhouse-Geisser, the other worked out by Huynh-Feldt (because we are approximating, there is no ideal solution). Epsilon is then used to calculate new values for the degrees of freedom, and these provide the new F distribution which is an approximation to the empirical one. This is then used to calculate the p value. When you do an analysis of variance using SPSS, the epsilon calculation is done automatically and the corrected p values are given. The simplest rule is to always use the Greenhouse-Geisser correction for the p value. Sometimes it is a little conservative, but not excessively so. By conservative we mean that, instead of holding Type I error at 5 per cent, it holds it at a *lower* value (e.g. 4 per cent).

SPSS exercise 3: one-way repeated measures ANOVA

Analyse the data file 1-WayWithin-SubjectsAnova.sav. You may wish to consult a book to guide you through the analysis in SPSS, or you can find a guide at The Open University's OpenLearn website (http://openlearn/) and on the DD303 website. Look at the epsilon corrections in the ANOVA table.

Summary of Section 5

- Analysis of variance assumes:
    - The data points are distributed according to the normal distribution (the normality assumption).

- The variance between groups is the same (the homogeneity of variance assumption.

- The observations are independent of each other (the independence assumption).

• Repeated measures analysis of variance is appropriate when a subject is tested several times in different conditions.

• Repeated measures make the additional assumption of sphericity.

• When the sphericity assumption does not hold, repeated measures analyses can be corrected using adjustments to degrees of freedom.

6   Making decisions under uncertainty

6.1   Drawing conclusions from statistical tests

You should be familiar with the basic idea behind using statistical tests. Inferential statistics such as are normally taught in psychology departments are based on the testing of null hypotheses.

The actual values of variance found in any random sample will always differ from other samples. As we saw in Section 3.3, an F ratio can take any value, even when there is no effect of conditions, and the null hypothesis is true. As you saw, there is a particular sampling distribution for the F statistic, which shows how likely it is that you will get a certain value or greater when comparing two sources of variance drawn at random from the same population. These F distributions are called the **central F distributions**. These are the F distributions normally tabulated in statistics books or calculated by computers, and they are the ones we use to look up the 'significance' of a result.

The basis of the null hypothesis test, therefore, is that we consider the value of our calculated F ratio against these central F distributions to see whether it is likely or unlikely that we have obtained such a result by chance. By fixing a certain level of probability, known as the α or Type I error probability, the number of times that a decision is made in error – which means rejecting the null hypothesis when it is in fact true – is held at a certain level.

I will now develop the idea of Type I error further by considering multiple comparison techniques.

6.2   Multiple comparison techniques

The discussion of Type I errors so far in this chapter has focused on a scientific decision being made in a single comparison. This we can call the **error rate per comparison (PC)**. When we are doing more than one comparison, each one has a chance of producing a Type I error. Across all the comparisons we do (i.e. the complete **family** of comparisons), each one increases the chance that we will make at least one Type I error. This is known as the **familywise error rate (FW)**. If you are doing very many comparisons, this familywise error rate can become large indeed.

We need to find ways of doing lots of comparisons if we are really interested in them, yet avoid making lots of erroneous decisions.

As well as the issue of multiple comparisons, frequently we plan in advance (according to our scientific predictions) to do a certain set of analytical comparisons of the data. These tests which we have specified in advance are known as **a priori comparisons** (the 'a' is often, depending on your view of Latin, pronounced 'ah' as when the doctor asks you to say 'ah').

Sometimes however we have a set of data and we have little idea in advance of, or are simply surprised by, the kind of results that emerge. We then find ourselves doing comparisons which we didn't think of in advance in response to the data we have collected. These new comparisons, devised after finding the data from an experiment, are known as **post-hoc comparisons**.

Let us consider this a little more. Suppose we have the four groups as we discussed in Section 3.3 of this chapter. There are 25 possible (simple) inter-group contrasts. These are listed in Table 4.11.

Table 4.11   All possible comparisons for four treatments

Pairwise comparisons	1 vs 2 comparisons	1 vs 3 comparisons	2 vs 2 comparisons
A vs. B	A vs. (B + C)	A vs. (B + C + D)	(A + B) vs. (C + D)
A vs. C	A vs. (B + D)	B vs. (A + C + D)	(A + C) vs. (B + D)
A vs. D	A vs. (C + D)	C vs. (A + B + D)	(A + D) vs. (B + C)
B vs. C	B vs. (A + C)	D vs. (A + B + C)	
B vs. D	B vs. (A + D)		
C vs. D	B vs. (C + D)		
	C vs. (A + B)		
	C vs. (A + D)		
	C vs. (B + D)		
	D vs. (A + B)		
	D vs. (A + C)		
	D vs. (B + C)		

With four treatment groups we can see in Table 4.11 that there are as many as 25 different contrasts, all of which can be tested. Indeed, if you were to do 25 such comparisons (and the comparisons were all independent) your chance of making at least one Type I error would have risen from 5 per cent to 72 per cent (72 per cent is calculated from $1 - 0.95^{25}$). Such a high chance of making a Type I error is clearly unacceptable, especially if tests are being done wildly and without having been planned in advance of the experiment. Even so, Scheffé has modified the analysis of variance to allow such multiple comparisons to be done. Basically, his procedure (the **Scheffé test**) calculates a new critical value for the F ratio against which the comparisons are tested. For four treatments, the new critical value is equivalent to a single comparison being performed at $\alpha = 0.052^*$. Using this critical value instead of the normal one ensures that the familywise Type I error rate is at most 5 per cent. So, if you felt like it, all 25 contrasts in Table 4.11 could be done and tested. However, such a procedure is highly unusual, and the Scheffé test is so conservative in order to deal with this extreme case that it is rarely used. This is because the new critical value is very high, and thus it is hard for any individual comparison to reach it. Most statistical packages continue to print its results however.

The majority of post-hoc comparison techniques don't attempt to cover the possibility of doing all possible contrasts. They usually concentrate on doing just the **pairwise comparisons** (these are the six in the first column in Table 4.11). The problem of the rising familywise error rate for doing several comparisons has been much reduced because only six tests are to be performed, rather than 25. Instead of the familywise error rate for the complete set of comparisons performed at $\alpha = 0.05$ being 0.72, it is only 0.26 (26 per cent is calculated from $1 - 0.95^6$) for the six. This is still a high value, but the problem of dealing with it is obviously much reduced.

One way to deal with this is to change the α level for each comparison. Suppose, with six comparisons, the alpha level for each one is set to 0.0085. This succeeds in keeping familywise Type I errors at 5 per cent. This is because $(1 - 0.9915^6) = 5$ per cent. The downside again is that the individual comparison level is conservative: so it is harder for the individual comparison to be significant. Indeed, the test is often little better than the Scheffé. There is a neat way of avoiding this problem, however, which relies on using sequential, conditional tests.

Note: Tests are conditional: subsequent tests are only made if tests in previous stages are significant

Figure 4.16 Sequential conditional testing (REGW-F) procedure

I will illustrate how this works with what is called the Ryan-Einolt-Gabriel-Welsh F procedure (usually referred to as the **REGW-F**, and you'll find it as that in SPSS). The means from the simple analysis of variance example (see Table 4.5, Section 3.3) are ordered as in Figure 4.16, lowest at the left and largest at the right. The procedure works by calculating the ANOVA F test across all four of the means (Step 1 in Figure 4.16), then if (*and only if*) that test is significant, the next step of the procedure is

---

* This is an asymptotic value (i.e. it is increasingly accurate as df (error) approaches infinity).

performed, which is to do another two F tests across sets of three adjacent means (Step 2 in Figure 4.16). If one of those tests is not significant, the procedure stops and those three means are declared equivalent. If the Step 2 F test is significant, the procedure moves to the next step and tests the two adjacent pairwise comparisons to see where the differences lie (Step 3 in Figure 4.16). Fortunately, SPSS does this procedure automatically when asked (see 'SPSS exercise 4').

Protection from familywise Type I errors comes from the sequential, conditional procedure. For example, the very first test is performed at $\alpha = 0.05$. If the complete null hypothesis is true (that there are no differences between *any* of the means), the procedure will stop 95 per cent of the time with a declaration of no significant differences. Only 5 per cent of the time will we proceed to do more tests, so we have held Type I error rates to 5 per cent (it doesn't matter if our subsequent tests erroneously identify more than one pair of means as different, the familywise error rate is defined as 'at least one' Type I error). The REGW-F procedure uses adjusted p values at each step to compensate for the sequential testing procedure, but this is all handled automatically by SPSS so we don't need to worry about how that is done.

The net effect of this analytical procedure is that we have searched for significant pairwise comparisons using an efficient sequential procedure.

SPSS exercise 4

Analyse the data file 1-WayBetween-SubjectsAnova.sav as a one-way ANOVA and ask for the post-hoc comparison REGW-F. You may wish to consult a book to guide you through the analysis in SPSS, or you can find a guide at The Open University's OpenLearn website (http://openlearn/) and on the DD303 website. Instead of selecting *Bonferroni* tests, select *R-E-G-W-F* instead.

6.2.1 Historical note on pairwise comparison techniques

The sequential procedure set out here can use any **omnibus test** procedure for differences among means. (Analysis of variance is an 'omnibus' test because it simultaneously tests for *any* differences between *all* the treatment means.) Another omnibus test is called the **Studentized Range** statistic which is very similar to the t test, but designed to work across a range of ordered means such as in Figure 4.16. The statistic it calculates is known as q. In SPSS, you will see a post-hoc procedure called REGW-Q. This is exactly the same analytical procedure as REGW-F, except it uses the Studentized Range q statistic instead of the ANOVA F statistic. In addition, there are several other tests suggested by SPSS for post-hoc comparisons. The following tests all use the same analytical procedure as REGW-Q: Neuman-Keuls, Tukey HSD and Duncan's range. The only difference between these procedures is their approach to making corrections to the p values during the steps. The REGW tests are recognized as being the most powerful tests which accurately keep the familywise Type 1 error rate low under all conditions. REGW-F and REGW-Q are very similar in power, perhaps with REGW-F just shading out REGW-Q, so the former test is my recommendation.

6.2.2 Special case: comparing multiple treatments to a single control (Dunnett's test)

If we want to restrict the post-hoc comparisons still further, there is a specialist test which is a little more powerful. If our experiments had a single control condition, and all the treatments need comparing to it, then we would be making fewer of the pairwise comparisons. For the data in Figure 4.6, if one mean was a control, we would only have three pairwise comparisons, instead of six as in Table 4.11. Again, we have reduced the opportunity for making Type I errors and that will assist us in controlling the familywise Type I error rate.

Dunnett's test (based on the t test) is a specialist test for this situation, in which Dunnett has developed a special t distribution (t_d) for the comparisons. Again, SPSS will perform this test automatically if requested.

6.2.3 Planned comparisons

Planned, a priori comparisons are those in which the analysis is dictated by scientific considerations. In other words, theoretical considerations have dictated which comparisons between treatments are being tested, rather than feelings which have arisen due to you seeing the means after the experiment has been completed.

Post-hoc comparisons are useful when you couldn't predict in advance what differences will appear between your conditions. But psychologists are often a little more insightful! If you know what you are looking for, you can be clear in advance which are the important *planned comparisons* out of all the possible ones (e.g. see Table 4.11), and this allows you to perform these few comparisons at the normal 5 per cent α level of significance.

Usually, the prediction made in advance involves some form of comparison between the conditions in the experiment. This is most easily seen by looking at an example. We shall look at the example from 'SPSS exercise 1: One-Way Between-Subjects ANOVA'. This used an experiment by Towell *et al.* (1986) in which participants, pretending to be jurors, were shown the testimony of an alleged victim of rape, and afterwards had to try to recall facts from the testimony. So the level of recall was measured. However, in three of the four conditions, the face of the witness was obscured: one condition covered her face with a grey blob, a second condition pixelated her face, and the third reversed her image like a photographic negative. In the fourth condition the witness's face was unmasked (normal).

Since the hypothesis was that the masking would reduce recall, the most powerful a priori (planned) comparison is the unmasked condition compared with the other three conditions taken together. This requires the use of **coefficients** to define the contrast, in this case –3, 1, 1, 1. The –3 coefficient is applied to the unmasked condition, and the 1 coefficients are applied to the three masking conditions.

SPSS exercise 5: planned comparisons

Perform a set of comparisons on the file 1-WayBetween-SubjectsAnova.sav.

You may find it helpful to consult a book to guide you in doing this in SPSS, or you can find a guide at The Open University's OpenLearn website (http://openlearn/) and on the DD303 website.

6.3 Type II errors, effect size and power

We have dwelt a lot on *controlling* Type I errors, making sure we don't make too many erroneous scientific decisions such that we wrongly conclude there is a difference between conditions when really there is none. The emphasis here is on *control*, because we as scientists take control over how many such errors we are prepared to make: usually it is 5 per cent of the time when the null hypothesis is true. When the null hypothesis is true, the size of the effect is zero, so a conclusion that there is a difference is an error.

But what if there is really an effect, so that the effect size is greater than zero? If so, we can't make a Type I error, since the null hypothesis is false. Are we therefore sure to find a significant effect? Unfortunately not. There is one more source of error, called a Type II error, in which we fail to detect a significant effect and erroneously accept the null hypothesis.

Unlike Type I errors, we don't have control over Type II errors, at least not in the same way. How often are we likely to make Type II errors? It depends on how big the effect is (the **effect size**) and how many participants we run. Large effects are easy to detect and mean we make few Type II errors even with modest numbers of participants. Small effects are hard to detect and mean we would need many participants (sometimes hundreds or even thousands) to give us a good chance of avoiding Type II errors.

Effect sizes are often measured by values related to correlation (r). A very common measure is **squared correlation** (r^2). In analysis of variance, the equivalent of r^2 is η^2 (eta-squared). It can take any value between zero (no effect, the null hypothesis is true) and 1 (all the variability between our measures has come from the conditions). It is worth paying attention to the effect size as it can tell us how big our effect is, and it is even possible to calculate the likely Type II error rate for an experiment. For example, the analysis of variance in 'SPSS exercise 1' produced an effect size of $\eta^2 = 0.3$. From this it is possible to calculate that an experiment which ran 80 participants in each group would have a Type II error rate of 20 per cent. In other words, such experiments would fail to get a significant result once in every five replications. This may seem to be a high failure rate, but is actually quite common among psychology experiments. For the Type II error rate to fall to 5 per cent, the experiment would have to run 120 participants per group.

Another way of looking at Type II errors is to consider **power**. Power is 1 – (Type II error rate). So if Type II error rate is 20 per cent, power is 80 per cent. We say an experiment has power of 80 per cent if it has an 80 per cent chance of detecting an effect of a given size. When we design experiments, it is obviously desirable to increase our power as much as possible, though this usually means running lots of participants, which can be very inconvenient.

Calculation of power is quite technical and usually done at advanced levels (beyond undergraduate degrees). Computer programmes are available to assist, however. A good one is G Power (Erdfelder *et al.*, 1996), which is available on the internet. Calculation of power is described well by the Erdfelder *et al.* article.

Summary of Section 6

- Type I decision errors are set at a particular level by the experimenter choosing a value for the alpha probability.
- Multiple comparison procedures are designed to reduce the total number of Type I errors to an acceptable rate for a family of comparisons. This is known as the **familywise error rate**.
- The different kinds of multiple comparison techniques differ in the number of different comparisons which they are testing, though all attempt to retain the same familywise error rate.
- Type II errors are failures to reject the null hypothesis even when there is truly a treatment effect.
- The sample measure of the effect size can be used to give an idea of the Type II error rate of an experiment.
- The power of an experiment is simply the converse of the Type II error rate (1 – Type II error rate).

7   Analysing data for the case where the independent variables are continuous

7.1   Simple linear regression

Analysis of variance involves partitioning the variance found for a dependent variable according to independent variables (factors) which are categorical (such as gender, handedness, or treatment situations such as drug treatments etc.). However, partitioning variance can also be applied when the independent variables are continuous (e.g. age of participant). The principles are almost identical to those in an analysis of variance, which is why regression and analysis of variance are considered to be two sides of the same coin. I shall illustrate this with a simple example for linear regression.

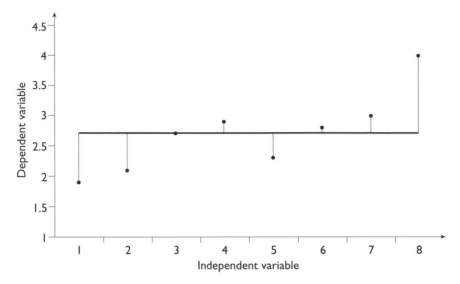

Figure 4.17   Eight data points from an experiment

Figure 4.17 shows another eight data points which have been measured on a dependent variable. Again, each data point varies from the grand mean by a certain amount. The variance of those data points about the grand mean can be calculated as before. As in Section 3.2 (Figures 4.1 and 4.2) of this chapter, giving you the information that these eight data points in Figure 4.17 fall into two groups would allow them to be measured according to Figure 4.18.

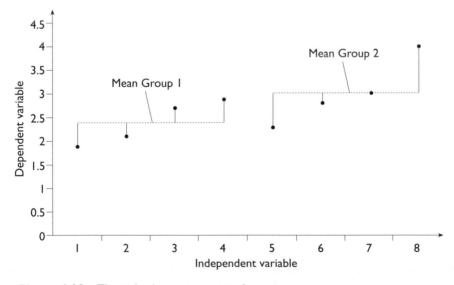

Figure 4.18   The eight data points treated as two groups

Here, with the data in two groups, each data point is found to vary about the mean for its own group. The residual variance can be calculated, and the reduction in variance tested with an appropriate F ratio. In regression, we are still interested in the reduction of variance, but now with information rather different from the categorical (group) information in Figure 4.18. Instead, we are told that the eight data points are in fact serially ordered from left to right across an independent variable.

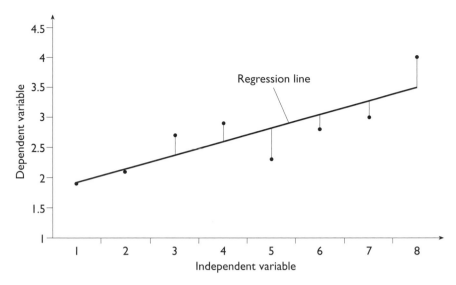

Figure 4.19   The eight data points treated as a continuous series

In Figure 4.19 the same eight data points represent measures taken at different points across a continuous independent variable along the horizontal X axis. Because the independent variable is continuous, we now want to know whether there is a continuous rise in performance on the dependent variable as we measure at different points on the independent variable. That is, we want to know if the data are well fitted by an upward-sloping straight line as shown in Figure 4.19. If we calculate a good straight line across the data points, we can then measure the distance by which each data point differs from that line. These distances, shown in Figure 4.19, are used to calculate the residual variance in the case of regression, just as differences from the individual group means were used in the categorical case (ANOVA). Once again, the residual variance will be somewhat less than the total variance around the grand mean, and an F ratio is calculated to test whether the reduction in variance found should be attributed to chance or not.

Spreadsheet exercise 7

Spreadsheet exercise 7 uses data for a linear regression over four points. The residual (error) sum of squares over the four points is shown. As in spreadsheet exercise 1, you can move the regression line, this time at both ends, so you can change its slope as well as its position.

Instructions

Open spreadsheet EX7 (Excel).xlsx (Microsoft Excel) or EX7 (OO).ods (Open Office). At the top there are two values which specify the two ends of the estimated regression line. They are labelled as 'Estimate: Left-hand point' and 'Estimate: Right-hand point'. Select each one and type in a new value. Increase the value of the left-hand point (e.g. to 7) and decrease the value of the right-hand point (e.g. to 2). You should see the error sum of squares go down, at least to begin with. As the error sum of squares goes down, the F ratio rises, eventually becoming significant. See if you can find the line with the least squared error (this is when the Error Sum of Squares = 1.2).

Thinking back to the fundamentals we considered in Section 3, as the above exercise illustrates, linear regression constructs a regression line that minimizes the squared error between the data points and the line: again the method is *least squared error*. Whereas in ANOVA we were using means (in groups) to minimize error, in regression we use a sloping straight line to minimize error. Both techniques use least squared error (Section 2.2) to arrive at estimates, and in both the variance is partitioned into that due to the independent variables and that due to remaining (residual) error. (This is because they are examples of what is called General Linear Modelling.)

7.2 Multiple linear regression

Simple linear regression measures the amount by which predicting from a linear function of a single independent variable reduces the variance in one dependent variable. Multiple linear regression is still concerned with reducing the variance in a single dependent variable, but in multiple regression there are several independent variables which are used to predict its values. The same principle, that of reducing (or conversely predicting) the variance in the data, still holds. You can perhaps begin to imagine how the concept of multiple regression is linked to analysis of variance, which we have also described as a mechanism for partitioning the variance in the data.

The extension from single linear regression to multiple linear regression is similar to the extension of one-way ANOVA (which has one 'factor') to multiple factor analysis of variance. Several predictor (independent) variables are used to predict the dependent variable, using least squares estimation of the slopes for each one. Let's look at a special example in which three predictors, which are overall measures extracted from rating scales, are used to predict a dependent variable.

Students at a large university in the USA were asked to rate the overall quality of lecturers on various courses, using a scale of 1–5 (5 being good).

We shall use this overall rating as the dependent variable, i.e. the one we want to predict from the independent variables.

For this exercise, we are using specially constructed independent variables calculated from a set of other ratings and data from the students. The first independent variable is general quality, which is a combination of several other ratings of quality that the students made. The second independent variable is knowledge and popularity, which combines the rating of lecturer's knowledge with the popularity of the course. The third independent variable comes mainly from the expected grade for the student (1 = low grade, 5 = high grade). How will these three independent variables predict the dependent variable?

When you perform the multiple regression using SPSS, you'll see that you include these independent variables in the same way as you include factors in between-subjects analysis of variance.

SPSS exercise 6

Do a multiple regression on the file courfact.sav. You may wish to consult a book to guide you through the analysis in SPSS, or you can find a guide at The Open University's OpenLearn website (http://openlearn/) and on the DD303 website.

When you do the multiple regression, make sure you specify:

Dependent variable = Overall

Independent variables = Genqual
                               Knowpop
                               Gradesiz

You should use the 'Enter' method and make sure you select *Descriptives*.

Table 4.12 Multiple regression results

Coefficients[a]

Model		Unstandardized Coefficients		Standardized Coefficients	t	Sig.
		B	Std. Error	Beta		
1	(Constant)	3.550	.050		71.574	.000
	General Quality	.432	.050	.705	8.627	.000
	Knowledge and Popularity	.265	.050	.431	5.282	.000
	Expected Grade	6.381E-02	.050	.104	1.274	.209

a. Dependent Variable: OVERALL

The table of results (see Table 4.12) gives several numbers for each independent variable. There are the main coefficients B and Beta. These are the *slopes* of regression lines (see Figure 4.19), as estimated by the least squares procedure. The B value is the slope of the regression line calculated on raw data. The Beta coefficient is the slope of the regression line calculated on the data after each variable has been *standardized* (a standardized variable has been changed so that its mean is 0 and its variance is 1). We shall see in a moment that the Beta coefficient has special properties.

Each independent variable is tested for significance by a t test. This, also, is exactly like analysis of variance in which every factor is tested with an F test. However, in regression each independent variable involves a single line (slope), and can only have one degree of freedom. In fact $F_{(1,n)}$ is the same numerically as $t(n)^2$, so the t test is used equivalently. If you want to stay working with F values, you can square the t value: it won't affect the p value at all. Finally, you will also see an 'R square' (r^2) value in the Model Summary. This is an effect size measure equivalent to eta-square (η^2) in analysis of variance. So multiple regression operates in basically the same way as analysis of variance, giving statistical tests for each independent variable. In this case, the statistical tests for the independent variables 'genqual' and 'knowpop' are both significant, so these factors had an effect. However, the third independent variable ('gradesiz') was not significant. The only thing missing, compared with ANOVA, is interactions between independent variables, and if you go on to do advanced statistics, you will find that these can also be evaluated.

7.2.1 Correlations and orthogonality

The above example is a special case of multiple regression, because the independent variables are **orthogonal**. This means the correlation between any of the independent variables is exactly zero.

Your analysis in 'SPSS exercise 6' produced the correlations between all the variables. Take a look at those correlations (see Table 4.13).

Table 4.13 Correlations between the variables

Correlations

		OVERALL	General Quality	Knowledge and Popularity	Expected Grade
Pearson Correlation	OVERALL	1.000	.705	.431	.104
	General Quality	.705	1.000	.000	.000
	Knowledge and Popularity	.431	.000	1.000	.000
	Expected Grade	.104	.000	.000	1.000
Sig. (1-tailed)	OVERALL		.000	.001	.236
	General Quality	.000		.500	.500
	Knowledge and Popularity	.001	.500		.500
	Expected Grade	.236	.500	.500	
N	OVERALL	50	50	50	50
	General Quality	50	50	50	50
	Knowledge and Popularity	50	50	50	50
	Expected Grade	50	50	50	50

As you can see, the three predictors do not correlate with each other at all (the correlations are zero). However, they do all correlate with the dependent variable. What do you notice about those correlations?

The correlations between each independent variable and the dependent variable are exactly the same as the Beta values. This only happens when the independent variables are orthogonal. In this special case, the Beta values are equal to the correlations between variables.

7.2.2 A more realistic regression problem

In reality, multiple regression analyses are almost always done when the independent variables are correlated with each other (i.e. they are not orthogonal). Let's look at a typical example. An investigation of children's spelling might examine the relationship between several psycholinguistic variables on spelling performance. It may attempt to predict children's spelling performance from chronological age, reading age, a standardized measure of reading ability and a standardized measure of spelling ability. These measures are all correlated with each other: we certainly expect chronological age to correlate with reading age, and the standardized scores are likely to correlate with each other too.

SPSS exercise 7

Once again, do a multiple regression, this time on the file multipleregression.sav. You may wish to consult a book to guide you through the analysis in SPSS, or you can find a guide at The Open University's OpenLearn website (http://openlearn/) and on the DD303 website.

Make sure you get the correlations as well as the coefficients table. Do *not* use the Stepwise Method (which has fallen into disrepute as a misleading technique for regression analysis).

Again, each independent variable is tested by a t test, and has both a B and Beta value. You can see from the correlations that the independent variables are correlated with each other. Now, the Beta values are *not* the same as the correlations. Why is this?

The correlations and Beta values are estimated in different ways. Correlations are estimated by correlating two variables directly: other variables are ignored as if they aren't there. But Beta values are calculated in a different way. The Beta value for each independent variable is calculated from the relationship with the dependent variable only after *all* the other variables have had their contribution removed. And if those other variables are correlated with the independent variable in question, it means some of its contribution has been removed with them. Only in the special case we looked at first, when the independent variables are not correlated at all, does the effect of an independent variable on a dependent variable stay the same whether other independent variables are being taken account of or not. So the correlations between the independent variables can be very important. In this case the correlations between the independent variables range from 0.124 to 0.793. Brace *et al.* (2003) suggest such correlations are acceptable, but the higher correlations are worrying: we don't really want to use variables which correlate as strongly as 0.793. All sorts of problems can arise: for example, the Beta values are 'unstable' and fluctuate wildly with only slightly different data. We could do with something that helps us decide whether there are grounds for excluding a variable.

7.2.3 Tolerance

The correlation matrix shows how two variables are correlated. To see if there is a problem with a particular variable, it would be more useful to have a measure of the correlation between one independent variable and all the other independent variables taken together. For example, in this case the standardized reading score has a multiple correlation with the other variables, taken together, of 0.859. This is a high value, and we probably would consider excluding this variable from the model. High multiple correlations can result in instability in the regression solution, sometimes resulting in no solution being found at all. In short, it gets harder to trust the results from the analysis.

I just said that the multiple correlation of the standardized reading score with the other independent variables was 0.859. How did I know that? Unfortunately, this obvious figure isn't provided by SPSS. Instead, we are given something called **tolerance**.

Tolerance is calculated directly from the multiple correlation, by squaring it (0.859 squared gives 0.738) and subtracting from 1 (1 − 0.738 = 0.262). So the tolerance for the standardized reading score is 0.262. As we've subtracted from 1, low tolerance values are bad news, and we ought to worry if they are less than about 0.3.

Tolerance gives a *statistical* reason for excluding a variable from an analysis. However, statistical reasons shouldn't automatically be used to override theoretical reasons. If we have reason (i.e. a theory or results from other experiments) to believe a particular variable is important, we should retain it and look elsewhere for problems or solutions. In particular, if we want to retain independent variables which have low tolerance, we will need large numbers of participants to try to increase stability in the estimates of the Beta coefficients. This is because independent variables with low tolerance make these estimates very unstable, which means the estimates vary widely from one set of data to the next.

So multiple regression allows us to consider continuous independent variables rather like factors in analysis of variance, but we need to be careful because, unlike ANOVA, these independent variables can be correlated, leading to potential problems with our results.

7.3   Analysis of covariance

You can think of analysis of covariance as simply a way of combining into one analysis effects due to continuous and categorical variables. It is worth pointing out the importance when constructing an analysis of using the appropriate forms for the factors and variables. It is a common practice among psychologists to treat continuous factors as if they are discrete purely for the convenience of being able to run an analysis of variance. For example, even when the data for the age of subjects are available, such as when running experiments on child development where children's ages are known, frequently the sample is cut into two or three groups such as 5 to 7-year-olds, 8 to 10-year-olds, and 11 to 15-year-olds. This produces a categorical factor with three levels which may easily be used in analysis of variance. However, as we shall see, this is a poor way of entering a continuous variable such as age which is certainly very easy to measure precisely (though, of course, there may be theoretical reasons for grouping children by age). Let us consider the data which are used to create the graphs in Figures 4.17, 4.18 and 4.19 in Section 7.1 of this chapter. The eight data points may represent eight subjects of different ages. The actual data are shown in Table 4.14.

Table 4.14

X	Y
1	1.9
2	2.1
3	2.7
4	2.9
5	2.3
6	2.8
7	3
8	4

If these data are appropriately analysed using linear regression, the F value for predicting the dependent variable Y from the continuous predictor X is 6.8, which with one and six degrees of freedom is significant at more than the 1 per cent level. But suppose the psychologist had chosen simply to divide the data according to a dichotomous classification as in Figure 4.18, whereby the first four data points are grouped together and the second four data points are grouped together. Now, the F statistic produced by this grouping is only 3.1, which with one and six degrees of freedom is not even significant at the 5 per cent level. Artificially constructing groups from something that is really a continuous dependent variable is a sure way to lose information in a set of data, and prejudices the likelihood of finding results in the analysis. Analysis of covariance allows the introduction of continuous dependent variables alongside categorical ones, which will allow easy interpretation by the psychologist. We shall look at an example of this in a computer exercise.

Let us first finish considering what in fact happens when the data in Table 4.14 are categorized into two groups. Effectively, the continuous variable is recoded with only two levels, such as in Table 4.15.

Table 4.15

1	1.9
1	2.1
1	2.7
1	2.9
2	2.3
2	2.8
2	3
2	4

This makes it obvious how the continuous variable has been collapsed to only two values. Indeed, you may consider it instructive to treat this as a simple linear regression and perform the regression predicting the values of the dependent variable from the new X values, even though there are only two possible numbers. If you do such a regression, you will find exactly the same result as you get from the analysis of variance (or t test) with a dichotomous factor. This again emphasizes the correspondence between analysis of variance and linear regression. Indeed, in effect what happens in analysis of variance is that a regression line is drawn between the two groups, as you can see in Figure 4.20.

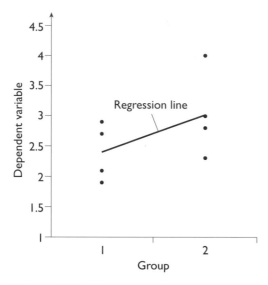

Figure 4.20   A regression line drawn through two groups

The regression based on the categorical variable formed in the analysis of variance is calculated in the same way as regression lines on the continuous variables in multiple regression. Therefore, when at all possible make sure that all the information in a continuous variable is used in the analysis.

SPSS exercise 8

Do an analysis of covariance on the file ancova.sav. You may wish to consult a book to guide you through the analysis in SPSS, or you can find a guide at The Open University's OpenLearn website (http://openlearn/) and on the DD303 website.

One final point about linear regression models. If we evaluate models with continuous variables directly in the analysis, we are only looking for linear relationships. If the actual relationship between the predictor and the criterion variable is not a straight line but a curve, then our model will be less able to detect the relationship (in much the same way that incorrectly analysing a linear trend, such as Figure 4.17 in this chapter, as a dichotomous variable – as in Figure 4.18 – weakens the analysis). It may result in no relationship being found at all. So you should always do scatter plots of your data to see if the trends are linear or decidedly curved. If they are curved, you'll need to come up with a more sophisticated analysis.

Summary of Section 7

- Multiple linear regression, analysis of variance and analysis of covariance are all techniques for partitioning the variance of a dependent variable according to a number of predictor variables.
- These predictor variables may be categorical ('discrete') or continuous. Analysis of variance deals with designs involving factors which are all discrete.

Multiple regression and analysis of covariance are ways of analysing the variance with predictor variables which are both continuous and discrete.

- Where possible, if a dependent variable has been measured continuously, it should be used in a statistical model in a way which retains that measurement.
- In many regression problems, especially multiple linear regression, the predictor (continuous) variables are correlated with each other – that is, they are not orthogonal.
- Non-orthogonality among predictor variables means that results of the analyses must be interpreted with care, and may make it necessary to exclude variables if tolerance is low.

8   Conclusion

In this chapter you have learned that the basis of parametric statistics is to produce parameters (or estimates, such as the mean) which have least squared error. From this concept emerge the analytical techniques of analysis of variance, multiple regression and analysis of covariance. All these techniques are ways to formalize how we make decisions on the basis of experimental data. We always want to make the best decisions we can, but don't forget that we are engaged in a scientific endeavour, and the result of a statistical test is always only a part of the information we use.

Always make sure you are using these tests in the most appropriate way. As the old adage says, there are lies, damned lies, and statistics ...

Further reading

Howell, D.C. (2002) *Statistical Methods for Psychology* (5th edn), Belmont, CA, Duxbury Press (imprint of Wadsworth Publishing Company/a division of International Thompson Publishing Inc.).

References

Brace, N., Kemp, R. and Snelgar, R. (2003) *SPSS for Psychologists* (2nd edn), Basingstoke, Palgrave Macmillan.

Erdfelder, E., Faul, F. and Buchner, A. (1996) 'G Power: a general purpose power analysis program', *Behavior Research Methods, Instruments and Computers*, vol.28, no.1, pp.1–11.

Towell, N., Kemp, R. and Pike, G. (1996) 'The effects of witness identity masking on memory and person perception', *Psychology, Crime and Law*, vol.2, pp.333–46.

Appendix: Personal data: a guide for DD303 students

What is personal data?

Personal data is any information can be used to identify a living individual. Personal data includes names, addresses, email addresses, personal identifiers, photographs etc.

Whether you are collecting personal data via a questionnaire, telephone, email or face-to-face, please make sure that you comply with the following guidelines:

- inform the people who you are ('I'm David Jones, a student with The Open University')

- the reason why you are collecting the data ('As part of my studies I am researching ...')

- assure them that the data will only be used for research purposes

- that it will form part of an anonymized report

- that it will not be passed on to any third party.

If, after informing them of the above, the person is happy to answer your questions, then they have given their consent to the purpose(s) for which you are collecting the data.

Consent

Informing people of the purpose for which you are collecting their data and obtaining consent is very important in order to comply with the Data Protection Act 1998, as individuals must not be deceived or misled as to why the information is needed.

The Data Protection Act 1998 regulates the processing of personal data (information relating to living individuals). The definition of data has been widened to include certain manual records and the definition of processing to include anything done with data from obtaining through to destroying.

The Act exempts personal data used for research purposes from certain of the Data Protection principles, but there is no blanket exemption. Research must meet one of the conditions specified in the Act and those relevant are:

1   the individual has consented to the use of the data for research. It should be noted that in particular that the processing of sensitive personal data (such as ethnic origin, physical or mental health) is subject to stricter controls and requires the explicit, i.e. fully informed consent of the individual for research use;

2   the processing is necessary in pursuit of the University's legitimate interest. This does not apply, however, if the processing is prejudicial to the rights and freedoms or legitimate interests of the individual. In this case the individual retains the right to object to the processing.

Anonymizing data

The Data Protection Act specifically states that no processing of research data is allowed if the identity of a data subject is given away without consent, or if the data are used to support decisions in respect of an individual, or if there is likely to be substantial damage or distress.

Wherever possible, research data should be anonymized. The Information Commissioner encourages that where possible information relating to an individual which is not necessary for the particular processing undertaken, should be stripped from the personal information being processed. It does not amount to true anonymization but is in line with the requirements of the Data Protection principles. These are that personal data must be:

(a) fairly and lawfully processed and only if certain conditions are met;

(b) processed for limited purposes;

(c) adequate, relevant and not excessive;

(d) accurate;

(e) not kept for longer than necessary;

(f) processed in accordance with the rights of individuals;

(g) kept secure;

(h) not transferred to countries outside the European Economic Area without adequate protection.

Retention of data

The Act allows data that has been obtained solely for research purposes to be kept indefinitely. If you plan to keep original questionnaires and other personal data, then it must never be disclosed to a third party and must be kept securely to avoid accidental disclosure.

Right of subject access

Personal data processed for research purposes are exempt from the rules regarding subject access requests as long as the published research does not identify individuals. Discussing or divulging personal data between colleagues on a project does not mean that research purposes are exceeded.

Security

Once you have collected the data, you have a duty to keep it in a secure manner in order to prevent accidental disclosure, as it should only be disclosed on a need to know basis. This means questionnaires, disks, laptops or memory sticks etc. should be locked away in a drawer and not left out on a desk. Don't allow others to read personal data displayed on your computer screen, turn the screen away or minimize the window.

Using the data for other research projects

The Act states that research (including statistical or historical purposes) may legitimately involve further processing of personal data beyond the originally stated purposes. This is because data collected for one purpose in the course of an experiment or survey might later be seen to have other applications.

If you have any queries regarding the Data Protection Act 1998 and your research project please contact the Data Protection Office at The Open University.

Source: *Guidelines for Open University Students on the Use of Personal Data for Research Purposes*, July 2004

Acknowledgements

Grateful acknowledgement is made to the following sources:

Cover image
Copyright © Dave Ellison/Alamy.

Plates
Plate 6: George, M.S. 'Transcranial magnetic stimulation', *Scientific American,* vol.289, no.3, September 2003. Scientific American, Inc.; *Plate 8:* Damasio, H., Grabowski, T., Frank, R., Galaburda, A.M. and Damasio, A.R., 'The return of Phineas Gage: clues about the brain from a famous patient', *Science*, 264: 1102–1105, 1994, with permission of Hanna Damasio, Department of Neurology and Image Analysis Facility, University of Iowa. © 1994 AAAS; *Plate 9:* Tranel, D. *et al.* 'A neural basis for the retrieval of conceptual knowledge', *Neuropsychologia,* vol.35, no.10, 1997. Elsevier Science Ltd.

Figures
Figure 2.2: Courtesy of Ingrid Johnsrude; *Figure 2.3:* Opitz, B. *et al.* (1999) 'Combining electrophysiological and hemodynamic measures of the auditory oddball', *Psychophysiology,* vol.36, Blackwell Publishing Ltd; *Figure 2.8:* Adapted from 'Brief Introduction to FMRI', http://www.fmrib.ox.ac.uk.

Every effort has been made to contact copyright owners. If any have been inadvertently overlooked, the publishers will be pleased to make the necessary arrangements at the first opportunity.